RIVER AND

Front Cover: Springhead Pumping Station

British Library Cataloguing in Publication Data.
A catalogue record for this book is available from the British Library.

© Copyright Mary Fowler 1997

ISBN 0 948929 98 7

Published by

Highgate of Beverley

Highgate Publications (Beverley) Limited
24 Wylies Road, Beverley, HU17 7AP
Telephone (01482) 866826

Produced by

4 Newbegin, Lairgate, Beverley, HU17 8EG
Telephone (01482) 886017

RIVER AND SPRING

A chapter in the history of the water supply of Kingston upon Hull

by Mary Fowler

Highgate Publications (Beverley) Limited
1997

*Drinking fountain in Pearson Park, presented by Ald. J. H. Atkinson, 1864.
The text in the open Bible reads 'Whosoever drinketh of this water shall thirst again;
whosoever drinketh of the water that I shall give him, shall never thirst'.
The fountain cost £33.*

RIVER AND SPRING

It is remarkable that the little settlement at the confluence of the Hull and the Humber was able to survive, let alone develop into the town of Kingston-upon-Hull.

In its early days, after the Charter of Edward I in 1299, the town was virtually an island, bounded by river, estuary and town moat. Very few feet above the surrounding marshy land, on a strongly tidal estuary subjecting it to floods, Hull had, nevertheless, defensive walls, within which were houses, workplaces and, in course of time, two fine churches. For centuries Hull had a major problem, for, despite the abundance of adjacent river water, the inhabitants wished to have pure spring water to drink, and the source of that supply was outside the town on the chalk Wolds and guarded jealously by the nearby villagers. As Hull grew in importance and size, the Mayor and Burgesses repeatedly made application to the reigning monarch, and once even to the Pope, for the right of access to the spring water. The people of Anlaby, Willerby, Cottingham, and the area around were afraid that a major conduit draining the spring water down to Hull would diminish their own supply and if Hessle Haven warped up because of the lack of water, they would be without a proper harbour.

Royal Commissions, riots, deliberate pollution of the water and protest songs are all ingredients of Hull's attempts to get the spring water and the villagers' resistance to these attempts: stories which may be read in some detail in the older histories of Hull. However, by the 17th century, Hull was not only taking water without hindrance by means of a ditch, but also distributing it via a waterworks situated just outside the town walls. As the town expanded, especially to the west, another works was established in 1830 at Botanic, to pump spring water into the town.

An important episode unfolds between the late 1830s and the 1860s at a time when there was gradual spread of the necessary scientific knowledge to make informed judgements and of technical advance to put ideas into practice.

The old arguments had concerned the quantity of water supplied by the springs. Was there enough for both the people of Hull and those who lived in the villages where the springs arose? The controversies about quantity still persisted in the period about to be considered, but there were also new arguments about the quality of the waters derived from the river and the springs. Attitudes during this period slowly changed; some of the protagonists barely knew their ideas were changing and a few die-hards held fast to old beliefs, even as facts accumulated to prove them wrong.

The story of the development of Hull's water supply has been told in brief by men who were participants in the action in the mid-19th century. Ald. John Mayfield, for many years Chairman of the Waterworks Committee, wrote his memoirs of the time and published them in 1909. Ald. Charles Eccles sent a series of letters to the press after the controversies about

Stoneferry and Springhead had died down, and this correspondence appeared as a booklet in 1901. Richer sources for us today are the newspapers of the time, where almost verbatim accounts of various meetings and lively comment upon them, are to be found. Although, as one would expect, there are inconsistencies, I have chosen to rely heavily on the press accounts in order to show what information the reading public received. As today we acquire knowledge and modify our opinions through the media of television and the newspapers, then the press was alone in serving the same function. There are some distortions due to political bias, but through all the reports, from the 1830s to the 1860s, there is a rich tapestry of narrative, embroidered with brilliant sketches of the people involved in the drama, amid scenes of the life of the time.

THE SITUATION

Hull is in a shallow river valley on boulder clay, with the dip slope of the chalk wolds escarpment on its western side. The clay rests on the chalk strata, the slope of which, in the district to be considered may be judged today by the gentle gradient of Kingston Road from Willerby Square to the city boundary. The fall from Springhead to Stoneferry is about five feet.

In ancient times the River Hull ran into the Humber somewhere near the later entrance to Albert Dock, but, by the time of the Charter of Edward I in 1299, a new channel was already established and had become the River Hull we now know, with the village of Wyke built on a triangle of land at the confluence of the Hull and the Humber. Edward I enlarged the Haven because he wanted a reliable port, not only for commerce, but for the furtherance of his wars with the Scots. To the north of the new Kingston-upon-Hull was Sculcoates, to the west, Myton, and the village of Drypool was its eastern neighbour across the river. On a map the position looks good, and subsequent monarchs regarded Hull as a strategically placed port. About 1541 Henry VIII, using land on the east bank at the confluence of river and estuary, created the great Citadel which continued to be a garrison until the 1860s. At the same time he built the North Bridge, thus opening up the 'road to Headon', known today as Holderness Road, leading to the fertile lands of Holderness. On the face of it, then, Hull was a useful port, facing mainland Europe and all set for a successful future. Unfortunately, despite all the water around it, the town did not have a good natural fresh water supply.

There was the river. Tidal up to about nine miles from its confluence with the Humber, it was therefore salty at high tide, but its contributory streams from higher ground in the Driffield area produced fresh water on the ebb. Thus Sir Thomas Glemham had to correct Charles I in 1642 when the King thought he could break Hull by starving the inhabitants and taking their fresh water: 'Your Majesty is misinformed; for, though you may cut off from them the fresh spring that runs to Hull, yet the very haven is fresh at low water and every man can dig water at his own door; and they cannot bury a corpse there, but the grave first drowns him ere it buries him.'

There were also the springs which arise in the chalk wolds. Sometimes these springs would utter as little fountains or just ooze out of the ground. They occur in many places, Millington Springs and St. John's Well at Harpham being among them. Many springs in the villages immediately west of Hull, that is, Anlaby, Willerby, Wolfreton, Cottingham and Haltemprice were on the dip slope and the water, therefore, made its way down to the East both in natural streams and in artificial drainage channels dug to improve the quality of the land.

Over the centuries, the poorer people of Hull took water from the river or

Old archway, Little Lane, Humber Street, known as Watergate.
(Photograph, 1965)

3

dug for it as Sir Thomas Glemham said, while the better-off either attempted to get spring water from the western villages or, when that was not forthcoming, bought it from men who transported it across the Humber in boats from similar springs in the Lincolnshire Wolds. The old archway in Little Lane, Humber Street, which survived until knocked into by a lorry in the 1970s, was at one time thought to be the gate in the town walls where water carriers came into the town, and it was popularly known as the Water Gate. The practice of buying Lincolnshire water persisted through the 1850s, but was no longer needed after the Springhead works opened.

A FRESH START

On St. Valentine's Day, 1838, a special committee of the Hull Town Council was set up to enquire into the possibility of obtaining a more plentiful supply of water for the town. This brief and the tenor of contemporary press reports give the feeling that it was expected to be a short-lived, almost *ad hoc* group. Originally consisting of Messrs. Gresham, Atkinson, Prissick, La Marche, Blyth, Bell and Wilkinson, it was dubbed 'The Waterworks Committee' by Cllr. Tinkler the following November.

THE STORY SO FAR

The 1838 Committee inherited a long history of attempts to procure water for the town of Kingston-upon-Hull from the chalk springs, particularly those of Anlaby and Willerby. For centuries, the people of the western villages were in contention with the Mayor and Burgesses of Hull over the rights of the matter, and several violent incidents, some with bizarre features, have been recorded.

In 1402, a memorial to Henry IV had led to the cutting of Julian's Dike, 12ft. broad and 5ft. deep, from Springhead to Hull. This may have been the re-excavation of an old ditch. Over the years various names were used for the town's water conduit from the springs: Julian's Dike, Derringham Dike or the Spring Ditch, the latter having become the accepted name by 1838. The water it carried had not always been of good quality, possibly because (deliberate pollution aside) other drainage channels had been disturbed during its excavation. The existence of so many springs made drainage imperative unless the land were to be left waterlogged. A major east-west ditch made it impossible for some landowners to drain their property directly into the Humber; this was another ancient grievance. The Courts of Sewers which met in Hull and Beverley tried to maintain a balance between the interests of townspeople who needed fresh water and of farmers and landowners who, over the years, had tried to improve their land.

Old accounts often mention 'ditches' carrying the spring water towards Hull. A map of the area between Springhead and Botanic in the Hull Record Office, carrying the date 1849 and the name of the then Borough Surveyor, David Thorp, shows two parallel ditches coming down from Springhead. The more northerly stream arises from Julian's Well and is named the Darringham Dike; the other seems to derive from the Darringham Springs and is named Julian Dike, although this may be from Julian's Well also, as there is a culvert shown on the map joining the two. The Spring Ditch, being south of the road (now Spring Bank West) must be the old Julian's Dike, and, indeed, the now grassed area behind the houses from Springhead Lane towards Calvert Lane is called Julian's Walk, a name given some few years ago in this century.

The Spring Ditch came down from Springhead to Calvert Lane corner (in modern terms), then along Spring Bank West, Spring Bank and Prospect Street to the town moat. Since about 1558 the water had collected in a reservoir called the Bush Dyke, an area of 60 yards by 10 yards, part of the moat.

In 1613, Hull called in the assistance of three engineers, Richard Sharpeigh of Westminster, William Maltby of London and John Cayer of Nether-Loughton in Lincolnshire. They took a piece of ground outside the walls on a hundred year lease at a ground rent of five shillings (25p) a year, and by 1616 had constructed a waterworks in which the water was pumped up into two cisterns and thence by pipes to the town houses by means of a

Elm pipes at Yorkshire Water's Museum, Springhead; the footrule shows their size.

Photograph: Mr. A. McTurk. By kind permission of the Senior Keeper, Mr. D. W. Atkinson

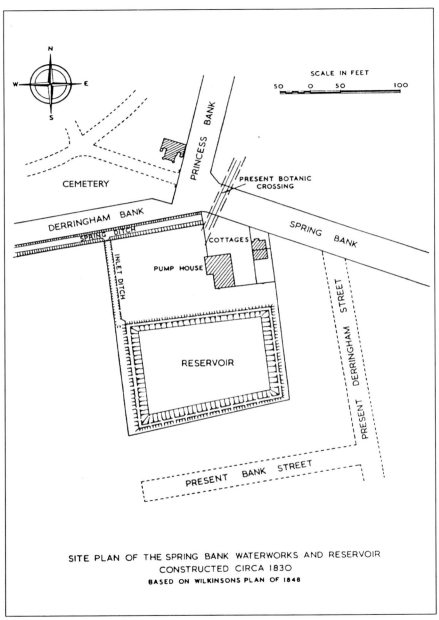

SCALE IN FEET

N
W   E
S

CEMETERY

PRINCESS BANK

PRESENT BOTANIC
CROSSING

DERRINGHAM BANK

SPRING DITCH

SPRING BANK

COTTAGES

INLET DITCH

PUMP HOUSE

RESERVOIR

PRESENT DERRINGHAM STREET

PRESENT BANK STREET

SITE PLAN OF THE SPRING BANK WATERWORKS AND RESERVOIR
CONSTRUCTED CIRCA 1830
BASED ON WILKINSONS PLAN OF 1848

Plan of the 1830 'Botanic' Waterworks.
From Kingston upon Hull Corporation Water Department booklet, 1970.

6

horse pump, a contrivance that was considered worth seeing by the diarist, John Evelyn. The engineers were at liberty to lay the pipes in the streets, so long as they dug up no more than ten yards by one yard at a time, made good after laying and before proceeding further. Early pipes were of elm wood called awms and were shaped at the ends like a pencil and pencil-sharpener to fit the sections together. Examples of these are to be seen at Yorkshire Water's Museum at Springhead. Lead string pipes took the water into the houses but only the rich had water in their homes; the poor continued much as before. The engine continued until 1773, when it was in the hands of one Megginson Wright, then steam power replaced the horses. To supply increasing demand, this, too, was superseded towards the end of the eighteenth century, by an expensive Boulton and Watt engine.

The legacy of this episode is a street name, Waterhouse Lane. Formerly Tan House Lane as shown on Thew's map of 1784, it had the waterworks at its northern end. By 1791, on Hargraves' map it is Waterhouse Lane, with Waterwork (*sic*) Street running parallel to Carlane (*sic*) and into Chariot Street, virtually enclosing the area that later would be used to build the City Hall. On Craggs' map of 1817 the rapid expansion of the town outside its original medieval area is seen and the waterworks buildings are surrounded by newer development. Engine Street had now appeared between the end of Waterhouse Lane and Waterworks Street, and its position, along the line of the later City Hall frontage, places the site of the waterworks in front of the present Punch hotel.

In February, 1830, the old waterworks were abandoned and new ones constructed near what is now Derringham Street on Spring Bank: referred to as the Botanic works. Water was conveyed into the town by underground pipes and the ditch to the town filled in, so that its site became a grassy area. Robert Wells, when Clerk to the Local Board of Health in 1852, reminisced about Spring Bank (which he had known from childhood) and he said there was then, just before the construction of the Botanic Waterworks, the open Spring Ditch from Hall Street to Botanic and four miles beyond that to Springhead.

The new engine-house had a thirty ton iron tank on top to hold 59,793 gallons, four times the capacity of the old town cisterns. Water came from the Spring Ditch into a large reservoir and was pumped up by a 20 h.p. engine to give a head of water for distribution. However much improved this may have seemed to some people at the time, there was no provision for the increasing population east of the River Hull and the report of the General Board of Health Inspector in 1832, the time of a major outbreak of cholera, condemned the supply as inefficient.

The Botanic works gave an INTERMITTENT SUPPLY, i.e. water was only available for a few hours each day, except Sunday, when there was none. Those who had water piped to their homes, stored the water in tanks and cisterns. There were taps in the streets and courts, but because of the imperfection of the piping system, often one street got more water than another, according to its distance from the main. Squabbles were not infrequent; some of these got as far as the Magistrates Court and were reported in the papers.

There were also wooden spigots on the mains at several points in the town to act as fire plugs, where leather hoses could be attached, but many workshops and factories had large tanks of water to be used in emergency, as well as smaller cisterns for daily use. The *Advertiser* of 31 January, 1840, reported the alarming appearance of a fire in the model loft of Messrs. Thomas and Wakefield Pim of English Street. The fire was soon put out 'by a flood of water thrown on it from the pipes attached to a cistern, containing upwards of 3,000 gallons, placed on the roof of the foundery.' The fire had been caused by an apprentice allowing candle snuffing to fall on shavings when shutting up for the night.

1838: RELATED MATTERS

At that time the QUALITY OF WATER was judged by sight, taste and smell and also by its hardness, for soap was still heavily taxed; despite Lord Althorp's reduction of the tax to 1½d (about ½p) in the lb. in 1833, the price was a check on its use by the poor.

The HARDNESS OF THE SPRING WATER derives from the chalk through which it has passed. The acidic action of dissolved carbon dioxide upon the chalk gives rise to the unstable calcium bicarbonate, which exists only in solution. Calcium bicarbonate reacts with soaps to give the calcium salt of whatever fatty acid was used to make the soap. An insoluble scum results and larger amounts of soap are needed for the cleansing process. Fortunately this type of hardness is temporary, as the calcium bicarbonate decomposes on boiling, leaving the water soft. The price is the deposition of chalk as scale or 'fur' in the vessel in which the water is boiled.

Inorganic chemical ANALYSIS OF WATER was effected by crystallising out dissolved salts from relatively large samples. Where salts would not crystallise out directly, they were precipitated in another form by a reagent and the amount of the original salt present was calculated by chemical equivalence.

There was, as yet, no true idea of THE CAUSE OF INFECTIOUS DISEASE. Pasteur, the most notable worker in this field, was moving towards a germ theory of disease during his work which disproved the spontaneous generation of microscopic organisms, but it was not until the mid-century, after important work on the diseases of vines and silkworms that he turned his attention to human infectious diseases.

The local newspapers, the Literary and Philosophical Society and the

1830 Waterworks Cottages near the former Botanic railway crossing.
Photograph: 1973

Mechanics' Institute were important CHANNELS OF COMMUNICATION. The papers reported fully, sometimes verbatim, the proceedings of meetings of the Town Council, the Myton Commissioners, the Sculcoates Commissioners etc. and also of the Lit. and Phil., the programme of which frequently included topics of immediate interest to the town; discussions following the lectures were among men who sometimes knew as much as the lecturers.

The town of Hull was now of much greater area and population than the old medieval triangle at the river mouth; there were new suburbs in the Albion Street districts, considerable spread into the old Myton, and the River Hull was becoming lined with factories, many concerned with milling of some kind. To accommodate the workers, recently come in from country districts to seek work in the town, small, huddled dwellings had sprung up near the factories, including some on the eastern side of the river.

1838: THE SEARCH FOR MORE WATER

With its brief of finding a more plentiful supply, the newly-formed Waterworks Committee started from the established fixed point, that is, the Botanic Waterworks. Five members of the Committee met on 27 February, 1838. They estimated that only about two-thirds of the Borough was supplied from the waterworks, but then, Hull had recently been enlarged through the boundary change. The Committee decided that any projected works should be financed from water rents and works, and thought that £1000 would be enough; they also directed the Town Clerk to ascertain upon what terms the Corporation held the springs; and Mr. Malam, experienced in such matters, explained what he had done in King's Lynn and promised to look at the present waterworks to see what economies could be effected.

The Committee's efforts after this seem hardly energetic. A plan of the water mains was sought and eventually obtained. A previous idea of getting water from the Cottingham Drain was resuscitated. Questions asked in the full Town Council meeting of 3 November, 1838, were answered by Mr. La Marche, who said they were anxious to find a new supply, and as some of the town's doctors were to analyse the water from possible sources, they had to wait for the Autumn rains to set in before preparing a report.

In fact, the Town Council was singularly unfortunate in its choice of members of this Committee as, by November, 1840, two had died, one became bankrupt and left the Council, another became insane. Until the end of 1841, there had been only six meetings when any real business was done and these were attended by three or four members only.

The use of the Cottingham Drain as a secondary source, basically to take the Wolds water by a ditch as from the Spring Ditch, was investigated more thoroughly and the possibility of laying pipes or tunnelling through privately-owned land adjoining Newland Tofts Lane (Princes Avenue) discussed by a deputation to the owners. Meanwhile the reading public was given little information via the newspapers. The quantity of water (or lack of it, rather) was the over-riding concern when the town's supply was mentioned. Occasionally fires were reported and sometimes the inadequacy of the fire engines was noted: further evidence that town water was in short supply.

The *Advertiser* of 7 August, 1840, reporting the Town Council meeting of two days before, stated that 'the Committee were endeavouring all in their power to secure an additional supply of water to the town, and that their measures for effecting this would as speedily as possible be brought to a conclusion.'

From the *Eastern Counties Herald* of 4 March, 1841, readers would learn that 'the Water Committee were drawing their labours to a close,' it being intended to increase the supply by a tunnel from the Cottingham Drain.

The first major move of the Committee came after its meeting of 20 December, 1841, when a formal request was presented to the full Council for the services of an experienced engineer, as the Committee 'were desirous of seeing the Holderness Ward supplied with pure water'. This marks the start of a more active phase under the chairmanship of Ald. Thompson. Whether or not the aspects of health and the quality of the water were stirring in the official conscience is not stated, but here, among the reports of the baths and the adverts for soap and filters, at last comes the expression 'pure water' as though the Committee had decided to go beyond its brief and invest in quality as well as quantity.

1842: ENTER MR. WICKSTEED

By March, 1842, the Water Committee was in correspondence with Thomas Wicksteed, of Old Ford, London, Member of the Institute of Civil Engineers, who had the management of the East Middlesex Waterworks and had superintended many other similar works in other parts of the country. He came to Hull the following month, and, with some of the Committee, surveyed the Waterworks, the present source of supply and several other proposed sources. It is clear from what emerged from Wicksteed's preliminary report, included in the Water Committee's own report of 15 August, 1842, that sources other than the Cottingham Drain had been discussed, if only informally. During his visit, Wicksteed told the Committee that the only reliable source was the River Hull at Stoneferry and the one he should recommend to be adopted, even though, in the words of the Committee's report, it was only a 'hurried survey'.

WICKSTEED'S PRELIMINARY REPORT, 26 May, 1842.

For a 'hurried survey' this contained a surprising amount of detail, as Wicksteed used not only his own observations, but had taken a great deal of information back with him to London, to be digested after the visit.

From what the engine-man at the Botanic works told him and from data obtained from a quick experiment he made at the Spring, Wicksteed calculated that when the Spring's supply was abundant, the quantity of water raised by the engine in six days, averaged 642,768 gallons per day over seven days; and assuming 6,000 houses to be supplied, this amounted to 107 gallons per house. When water was in short supply (about four months of the year), he reckoned the amount to be $75^1/_3$ gallons per day per house. Even this lower figure should be enough for domestic purposes, he said, but it was not so, because of the demands of industry, because of the inadequacy, on several counts, of the piping system and because of the method of distributing the water, trying to supply too many houses at one time.

To solve the problem of industry's demands was simple; until more water was available, cut off the water, refuse to supply the factories! (It was no new idea to provide houses with water before factories, etc. For example, the railway company's water was cut off early in 1841 so that houses in Belle Vue Terrace could be supplied.)

Wicksteed then gave an analysis of the 16½ miles of pipage from the waterworks and from the calculated velocity of the water deduced that 'a tenant who takes his supply from a service close to the mains will have 100 gallons delivered into his tanks in the same time that a tenant who takes his supply from the extremities of one of your long services is having 3 gallons delivered.'

The cheapest way of improving the supply, therefore, would be to take more branches from the main pipes, to reduce the excessive length of some of the service pipes, to have stop-cocks on all the branches (which would mean employing more turncocks to operate them), to open only a few stop-cocks at a time so as to alter the daily rota of supply and, lastly, to alter the proportions of the pumps so that they would give at least twice the present head of water (said to be 40ft. 6 ins).

He had found that 60 gallons per house per day was a sufficient though not over-abundant supply, from a one-week survey of 1,745 houses in a very respectable part of East London. Using 60 gallons as the average, he stated that if the Botanic works had been judiciously planned there was enough for 6,000 houses but not much more – and the present engine was grossly inefficient in the use of coal, being constructed on the worst principle for a pumping engine.

Therefore Wicksteed strongly recommended, that since an increased supply was necessary and desirable, especially in view of the fact that although 6,000 houses were already supplied, 7,000 were not, and assuming that eventually 20,000 houses as well as industry would need it, water should be taken from the River Hull.

ANALYSIS

A preliminary analysis by Mr. Pearsall, curator and secretary of the Hull Literary and Philosophical Society in the summer of 1842, and an analysis by Mr. Arthur Aikin, dated the following February, showed the river water at Stoneferry to be suitable for the purpose. Aikin, a London chemist, was sent 14 samples in stoppered bottles, Mr. Wicksteed instructing him to analyse three of them and make general examination of the rest. Of the three, Aikin said that he considered all to be good water, as they had less salts in solution than he had formerly found in the London New River water and that from the deep spring well at Whitbread's Brewery, 'both of which are acknowledged to be of good quality.' He admitted that rainy seasons and other causes might occasionally disturb the clearness of Hull water, but had no doubt that it would become quite fit for use by remaining still for some time in a reservoir. As the samples did not become foetid through the presence of organic matter when kept for some time, he offered no objection to the proposed use of the Stoneferry water.

It is significant that these analyses were chemical only. They revealed the presence of carbonates, sulphates and chlorides of sodium and calcium, some magnesium carbonate and also the unstable calcium bicarbonate, the cause of Hull water's hardness. Reference is made to organic matter, chiefly from plant growth and factory effluents. The term 'organic matter' and any reference to it is completely absent from Wicksteed's preliminary report and his subsequent letter to the Water Committee. In May, 1843, Pearsall said the amount of organic matter was very small (12-16 grains 'solid matter' to the gallon), whereas Aikin reported a few white fibres seen through a magnifying glass. The water was free of mud, Aikin said, and although it was impossible to ascertain the degree of organic matter, it was certainly there, for a brown residue which could be burnt off, was left when the water was evaporated to dryness.

The words fresh and pure, sometimes used in common speech to mean the same thing, must not be confused here. Fresh denoted the absence of salt, sodium chloride, and as the River Hull is tidal, obviously for some of its length and at certain states of the tide, the water is brackish, if not downright saline. 'Pure' water denoted water fit to drink. In hindsight, we perhaps shudder at the descriptions of what could sometimes be seen in the water, knowing what that might imply regarding the presence of microscopic objects. At the time under discussion, the harmful effects of unseen organisms was not even contemplated and so the consequence of drinking the water (what we should now call water-borne disease) was a connection not made, even by the most eminent doctors in the town. An hypothesis of the early 1830s had postulated tiny animals as the cause of cholera and suggested they were carried in water, but it was not until 1854 that Dr. John Snow first made a connection between a London water-supply and cholera, and still later, 1862, that Pasteur established the existence of bacteria.

1843: TO STONEFERRY

However hurried Wicksteed's preliminary report was, upon its findings and recommendations came the decision to establish a waterworks at Stoneferry and to abstract water from the river there. The Water Committee resolved on 7 September, 1842, that the Town Clerk should write to Wicksteed as soon as possible to ask him to come and proceed with the new waterworks. On the same day the Town Council met and, in its report on that meeting, the *Eastern Counties Herald,* after brief mention of Mr. Pearsall's analysis of the water, stated that there was 'prospect of an early and abundant supply being obtained from the river. New works will be required and immediate application is to be made to Parliament for the necessary powers.'

The Public Notice announcing the Council's intention to seek a Parliamentary Bill for the proposed works was dated 31 October, 1842, and appeared in the papers several times during November.

Wicksteed's main report did not appear until April, 1843. In it he reiterated points made in the preliminary report, using more accurate figures of water supplied, population etc. Although his earlier report had been based upon inaccurate figures, he found that the more up-to-date information served to strengthen his arguments. Taking figures from the 20 October, 1841, population returns and from the rate books, Wicksteed calculated that out of 15,293 inhabited houses only 9,797 were supplied with water.

The greatest supply per house per day was 56¼ gallons.

The least supply per house per day was 45½ gallons.

The average supply per house per day was 52¾ gallons.

– much below the previous estimates he had made on his first visit.

In fact, even the revised figures were high, because the average had to include the factories, water used on fires and that which ran to waste. Wicksteed, however, regarded the 'waste' water as anything but, 'as its running into the sewers was conducive to the Salubrity of the Town'.

An experiment supervised by Wicksteed's assistant during the period September 17 to October 13, 1842, showed that the daily amount of water from the springs was less than 17% of the proposed output of the new works where the source was inexhaustible. Wicksteed believed that the springs' supply could be doubled by a deeper bore, but still would not give enough water – say one third of the average required or only a quarter of what was needed in hot weather. Further, even if the springs could be made to yield more, a pumping engine would be needed there to raise the water to the surface and another at Botanic to give an adequate head of water for distribution. Such improvements would be uneconomic if in future the springs failed to supply enough for the town as it would grow. His proposals for Stoneferry were to supply Hull, both East and West of the river, until 1880.

Calculations from the population returns showed an increase in the East Riding population in the 1831-41 decade of 14²/₃%. Such an increase in the population of Hull in future years would mean that there would be at least 224 more houses to be supplied with water each year. The Stoneferry works were projected to supply the increasing number of Hull residents with 101 gallons per day per house, 'unless the population of the Borough should increase in a greater ratio than it has during the ten years ending 1841.'

PUBLIC OPINION

It was not until April, 1843, that public reaction reached the press. As reported in the *Eastern Counties Herald* on 6 April, the Town Council had had considerable discussion about the Waterworks Bill the day before, but the meeting was adjourned pending the arrival of Wicksteed's main report. Then the Bill's clauses could be studied, one by one. Even at this early stage the Council declared it had no intention of raising the water rents; a clause to that effect had already been inserted on the advice of Lord Shaftesbury. The adjourned Council meeting went into a third sitting and there was evident urgency, for, as the *Herald* told its readers, 'The Bill must be ready for progress through the Commons on the 24th, or it cannot pass this session.'

The first letter from a member of the public, in its way critical of

Wicksteed's proposals, was published in the *Herald* on 27 April, 1843. The writer suggested the springs be tested with an engine of a few horse power to see if the levels sunk appreciably after some hours. If they did, it could be assumed the springs were subject to exhaustion; if not, it was only a matter of raising the water high enough for distribution, to provide an adequate supply. By the following week, Wicksteed had refuted this idea, in a letter to the Waterworks Committee, read in Council. He believed the output of the springs could be doubled, but still doubted that they could provide an efficient supply for the whole town. Discussion at this Council meeting gave Dr. Joseph Ayre, an authority on the cholera, an opportunity to voice his favourable opinion on the river water at all seasons of the year, an opinion he would adhere to even in face of the terrible effects of the 1849 epidemic.

In the same issue, 4 May, 1843, the *Herald* carried a long and detailed comment on Wicksteed's latest report, as it was the most important local news of the week. A comprehensive description of the proposed Stoneferry works was given in a positive and favourable manner. Then . . .

'. . . we have a serious fault to find with the report.'

Wicksteed intended the Stoneferry works to be able to provide Hull with water until 1880. By that time, he forecast, using the percentage rise in population derived from the East Riding figures, there would be about 24,000 inhabited houses in Hull. The *Herald* based *its* projections on the *urban* population figures, which had risen far more steeply than the largely rural East Riding. The *Herald*'s editorial declared that the figure of 24,000 would be reached, not in 1880, but in 1861, giving the new waterworks only sixteen years before it reached its peak, instead of Wicksteed's 37. 'Suppose the Act to be obtained, and the works commenced, two years will be required to complete them. Then suppose, in 1861, in round numbers, 24,000 occupied houses, instead of the latter number in 1880, the works will be in full employment in 16 years from the time of completion instead of 37 years as estimated in the report. Whether this should induce the Corporation to extend their plan, we leave for the consideration of that responsible body, and also the consideration of the inhabitants. Does it not clearly show the necessity of something being speedily done?'

A public meeting convened at the request of a group of residents, many of whom were known to be Tories, was held at the Town Hall on Saturday, 6 May, 1843, at noon, with the Mayor, John Atkinson, in the chair. A motion by Charles Frost, seconded by Robert M. Craven, two of those who had instigated the meeting, that a committee should be formed to meet with 'the committee for the Bill', ostensibly to alter the Bill amicably so that it would have a smooth and therefore less expensive passage through Parliament, was really a delaying tactic. After discussion, John Wade proposed an amendment approving the exertions of the Water Committee, especially on behalf of the people of the Groves, Southcoates and Drypool, all east of the river. At least one man spoke bluntly. The Reverend E. Higginson said that after the Town Council had very properly deputed the matter to the Water Committee and then to a sub-committee empowered to employ Mr. Wicksteed, 'the first engineer in waterworks in Europe – if not in the world,' notices of this Bill had appeared during the autumn and no opposition was made. 'But, at the last moment, when the measure was about to become law, opposition arose, which, if effectual, could postpone the measure at least one year.' Wade's amendment was carried; Frost's motion was never put, but Ald. Thompson, Chairman of the Waterworks Committee, offered to listen to suggestions from Frost *et al* as the Committee's only object 'was to make the measure as complete and advantageous for the whole town as possible.'

Those against the Bill were particularly against the clause which appeared to show the town would make a profit out of the water undertaking, instead of the benefit going back to the customer. The clause derived from the following in the Water Committee Report of 15 August, 1842: that after all the expenses for the Act and Works be fully discharged, 'the clear net annual income derived from the sale of water from the present and contemplated waterworks to the extent only of £2,600 be in each year paid to the Borough Fund'; (the figure was rounded up from the previous year's net receipts of £2589). This payment to the Borough Fund was incorporated in the Bill and became a feature of the town's finances. As far on as 1898 when the details were no longer remembered by the then councillors and the expression 'milking the Waterworks Committee' was used, the Town Clerk of the time, Mr. E. Laverack, explained that the payment was a permanent charge on the Waterworks Committee ever since the 1843 Act which empowered the construction of the Stoneferry Waterworks.

Despite last-minute opposition, the Act for procuring water for the town of Kingston-upon-Hull made its progress through Parliament and received the Royal Assent on 12 August, 1843. Wicksteed arrived in Hull soon after and his first concern was again to test the springs 'so as to place the question beyond all manner of doubt.' The results agreed within 2% of his former experiment, thus confirming (to him) that the springs could supply only one day in seven, or, during drought, one day in ten.

All was ready to buy the land and start work at Stoneferry.

PUBLIC HEALTH

From this time onwards the Water Question became increasingly involved with general considerations of public health. In November, 1843, Edwin Chadwick and James Smith of Deanston visited Hull as members of the Health of Towns Commission. Their questions were searching and their energy immense in visiting each little court and alley of poorer districts of the town (even to the Thieves' Reading Room in Mill Street) to find out what exactly was the state of things in Hull, as part of a nationwide survey. The local papers, in their close small print published all the questions that were asked. During the same month, the usual quarterly tables of mortality appeared in the press and for the 13 weeks ending 30 September, 1843 the mortality rate in Hull was 3%. 'All towns in which the mortality exceeds 2% are considered unhealthy, and the causes which contribute to the excess are deemed susceptible of removal by improved drainage, ventilation and other measures.' In the Commissioners' survey were 18 questions about the water supply, all printed in the *Herald* with the added note, 'The disputed Waterworks question will thus claim the attention of the Commissioners visiting Hull. The Health of Towns Commission includes among its members, some of the highest engineering and chemical talent in the country; and we rejoice that so important a question as the supply of a large town with pure water will be brought before a body of gentlemen so highly qualified to advise the inhabitants, divested as they are of the local interests or prejudices, which often stand in the way of local improvements.'

The Commissioners were apprehensive that the Stoneferry works now in progress 'may not be found to afford a supply commensurate with the growing wants of the population. It will thus appear,' commented the *Herald* leader of 23 November, 1843, 'that the investigations and inquiries of the Commissioners have led them to form larger conceptions of the supply of water necessary for the health and comfort of large towns, than those which are generally entertained.' The Health of Towns Commission was, therefore, as well as an inquisitorial, an educational force, as the reading public, especially the well-to-do, began to have higher expectations of what was possible of a water supply.

In the Victorian period cleanliness of mind and spirit were important consequences of physical cleanliness and it was not uncommon to find comments on public morality mixed with reports on public health, such as (all from the *Herald*):

30 November, 1843: 'A little surveillance over building homes for the poor, might lead to less need to build prisons . . . Sanitary improvement should preceed education, must go hand in hand with religious instruction.'

1 August, 1844, just after the first report of the Health of Towns Commission was published, the editorial referred to 'the crime and immorality which can now be traced *with mathematical certainty* to the defective sanatory arrangements.' (My italics)

8 August, 1844: 'An abundant supply of good water is more nearly connected with morals as well as the health of the people than many persons will suppose.'

But,

23 October, 1844 at a meeting in the Mansion House in London, for instituting baths and washhouses for the labouring classes, Archdeacon Wilberforce (who became known as 'Soapy Sam' for his campaigning in

this cause) said, '. . .in answer to the charge that the poor love their 'wallowing in mire' and will not choose to be lifted out of it – that they covet their title of 'the great unwashed' . . . it is not true that the poor man is indifferent to cleanliness. The reason why some people are led to suppose [this] is, that *the poor are patient.*'

The 1842-43 programme of the Lit. and Phil. included many lectures on aspects of public health, or discussions of other scientific subjects turned in that direction as the matter was uppermost in people's minds. For example, in January, 1843, Dr. Humphry Sandwith on 'The Health of Large Towns' included consideration of water supply, sewerage, ventilation, paving, etc. and voiced the idea that 'a medical police ought to be appointed, with powers to enter premises to ascertain whether they were in the state of cleanliness, ventilation &c which health required.' This was one of two lectures Sandwith gave to the Society; they were wide-ranging on public health concerns and followed by animated discussion. Dr. Ayre and Mr. R. Craven stated that fever was scarcely known in Hull, but Dr. Sandwith's short experience here was to the contrary and he 'was astonished to hear medical men talk of fever as being the only disease arising from imperfect sewerage . . .'

Reported on 23 November, 1843: A discussion at the Lit. and Phil. followed a description of a drain flushing system used in Holborn. Mr. Robert Craven observed that in Hull 'every month or oftener'. a trap was opened to allow a flood of water through the main sewers in the old town. But he thought 'animal miasma' abounding in the tight courts and alleys was more detrimental to health than the drainage. This was a time when people thought a miasma or malaria (literally, 'bad air') was the cause of infectious disease, an idea which continued well into this century among the less well-informed, that a bad smell could cause infections and skin eruptions of various kinds.

Eastern Counties Herald, 8 February, 1844, again at the Lit. and Phil., Dr. Ayre, in giving the second of his lectures on 'Popular Errors' recalled that in 1817 he had visited Blanket-row where typhus prevailed to an extent that he had never witnessed either before or since, and which he attributed to drains running into an open cesspool. But, he said, the mere smell of decomposition of animal matter does not alone 'generate the malaria which generates fever' and he cited a particularly smelly episode near the Greenland yards, from which no-one took fever. None of the forms of continued fever were, in Dr. Ayre's opinion, infectious, even malignant cholera.

The GREENLAND YARDS EPISODE is a story worth repeating, for it shows, in its conclusion, how sanitary reform was delayed. A ship came in from Shetland, laden with about 100 tons of putrid whales – bottle noses and finners – with the fins and tails of other fish, for sale as manure. As it lay in the Old Dock (Queen's Dock) on the Saturday, the Dock Master contacted Mr. Barkworth, Magistrate, to see if the Dock Co. had the power to remove the vessel. Mr. Barkworth went to the Dock Office and found Mr.

Beadle, the Chairman, and Mr. Charles Frost, Solicitor to the Dock Co., who said the power lay with the Magistrates via the local bye-laws, which might mean ten days' notice would have to be given for removal of the nuisance.

The ship then moved into the river near the Charterhouse, where Police Inspector Tacey visited her and found the stench very bad. Mr. Firbank, also a Magistrate, who lived on Charlotte Street (the continuation of George Street towards North Bridge), said that when they opened the windows for air on Sunday, 'the smell was fit to stifle us'. Mr. Barkworth went further; he said the stench was sufficient to breed a pestilence.

The nearest bye-law to fit the case was one which carried the penalty of a fine upon anyone introducing a hog stye or anything else causing an offensive smell in or near a street or public path. The Justices, on information, must give ten days' notice of removal and a £5 fine for every day after the notice, that the stench remained. 'During the ten days', the *Herald* observed, 'a pestilence may be spread abroad which any fine that may be levied cannot remedy.'

The Captain was summoned before the Magistrates. Insp. Tacey in evidence, said that where the crew ate, drank and slept was without inconvenience, the smell there being comparatively trifling to what it was on shore, being carried from the vessel by the wind; but a Police Sergeant from Beverley Road said he felt sick from the stench. Capt. Dean said he wanted to go up river to Mr. Newmarch's yard near Sculcoates Church and bury the cargo, leaving it to rot the flesh off the bones. The Magistrates said the effluvium would rise through the ground and they would not allow the cargo to be deposited in the Borough. 'He ought,' they said, 'to have provided a place for it before he arrived', and they advised him to take it up the Trent or the Ouse to sell it to some of the farmers who would be glad of it. (Today's headline would have used the expression NIMBY, no doubt.) On being told he would be fined £5 per day if he did not remove the nuisance, the Captain hurried from the court.

The incident was discussed at length in the Town Council meeting of 4 October and the idea mooted of forming a bye-law to reduce the ten days' notice. Dr. Ayre, in his capacity as Councillor this time, said this smell was not injurious to health. The general opinion was that no bye-law could be framed that would not be injurious to trade. It was referred to a committee, but the whole business fizzled out and nothing was done after the Council meeting of 5 October, when Dr. Ayre again declared the smell was not harmful to health. The smell, however offensive, was entirely animal; putrefactions of animal and vegetable matter when combined become dangerous, according to Ayre, but a putrid animal effluvium alone was not so. Again it was said that no bye-law could be devised that would not injure trade and so the matter was withdrawn.

The most sinister aspect was Mr. Newmarch's field. Capt. Dean knew he could bury the stuff there, so what had been buried before? And where did the field drain? – Into the nearby river Hull, upon which, not so far away a brand new waterworks was being constructed to supply Hull with pure water until the year 1880.

In the lectures and discussions at the Lit. and Phil., the views of many local medical men were aired; sometimes the water supply became the focus of attention and piecing together what was reported in the papers gave insight both into the personalities of the doctors, many of whom were sometime town councillors, and upon which side they would campaign in what was rapidly becoming the great springs v. rivers controversy.

For opposition to the Stoneferry scheme was growing.

TORY OBJECTIONS

Agreement for the purchase of the land had been reached in the middle of September, 1843, and the site, in Cottingham Parish, at the bend of the River Hull at Stoneferry, was acquired from Mr. John Breeding, Marmaduke Prickett Esq., and Sir Thomas Coltman. Mr. Prickett was paid £695 for 6 acres. In modern terms, the site lay to the north of Clough Road, near the bridge, with Reservoir Road (another street name legacy) running through it.

Mention of money in the Waterworks Committee report to the Town Council meeting at the beginning of November, 1843, provoked questions from Messrs Harris and Tall, both Tories. Money was being raised for the project by loans and the Committee had taken up various sums at 4%. Harris said he had seen an advertisement for an insurance company, advancing money for Lincoln Gaol at 3½%. Ald. Thompson, the very active and committed Chairman of the Waterworks Committee, replied that they had dealt with a London money agent who would have known about the 3½% offer if it were available. Mr. Tall asked about the plans. Thompson replied that they had been open for inspection in London. Tall said, 'Strange!' He thought there were Hull builders who could have done the job and they should have had an equal opportunity with London firms. Again Thompson replied. Everyone was on an equal footing, knew where the plans could be inspected and had they been in Hull, Wicksteed would have had to be retained at a cost of five guineas a day. Duplicate plans to be shown in Hull would have cost £500.

Tall became somewhat direct in his comments, whereupon Thompson defended the proposed works. 'It would more than pay for itself. The work thus calumniated was one of the greatest and best ever devised for the town and the day would come when those who most opposed it, would return the greatest thanks.' Mr. Tall: 'It is one of the greatest jobs-' (order, order). The Mayor requested that this irregular conversation might end.

Ald. Thompson came in for more Tory sniping at the Council meeting of 2 January, 1844. Mr. Ward 'thanked Mr. Thompson for letting the Council know so much of the 'hot haste' in which things were managed by the Property Committee and he should like to know whether the Waterworks job had been carried through in the same way. (A laugh and cries of order, order)'

MEDICAL OPINION

The medical men, being closest to any knowledge of the cause of disease, argued the case for and against the river as a source of pure water.

DR. JAMES ALDERSON, in favour of retaining the use of the springs, wrote to the Mayor about the new waterworks, 'being anxious', reported the *Herald,* 8 February, 1844, 'now that the measure is finally adopted, to endeavour to mitigate as much evil and extract from it as much benefit as the case will allow.' He believed that in the present state of the river, no impartial man could for an instant contend that the water was salubrious. He suggested taking out one source of the river's pollution, that from Beverley, by diverting the Beverley sewers into the Barmston Drain instead of falling straight into the river. 'And as the machinery in connection with the springs is in full operation, the water approved, and as the collection of rates must be the same from whatever source the water is supplied, I conceive that the inhabitants have a right to expect that the present works should be continued, and a choice permitted of the source from which they may prefer to receive supply.'

DR. AYRE was strongly in favour of the river and in his 'Popular Errors' lectures cited the fact that for many years the water drunk by many in Witham and the Groves district came from the river, sometimes from the foot of North Bridge. He admitted that it was not as likely to be as free from impurity as at Stoneferry, yet it had never been found to be unfit or unwholesome. As to Beverley sewage, Ayre said it was first received into Beverley Beck and there held behind lock gates so that impurities rapidly settled before ever it reached the river proper.

DR. HORNER, in comment after Ayre's lecture, said he thought the use of the river water would be £200 a year in Ayre's pocket. Horner was a committed supporter of the use of the spring water and published a handbill, 'The Water Question' on 12 March, 1844, a copy of which may be seen in Yorkshire Water's Museum at Springhead.

DR. HUMPHRY SANDWITH, a comparative newcomer to Hull, writing to the *Eastern Counties Herald* on 18 March, 1844, began his letter, 'Party spirit in this town is the bane of everything . . . What reasons of public utility can be pleaded by the Waterworks Committee for refusing a compromise with the influential minority who object to their undertaking?' He was at a loss to see why the use of the springs should not be retained. Sandwith's argument, given in a long letter, was briefly this: he agreed with Horner that all the liquid refuse in the River Hull was harmful, but disagreed as to its main source. Sandwith said that Beverley's contribution was small in comparison with that from the district between Stoneferry and North Bridge and also Beverley's contribution was rendered harmless by flowing from Beverley to Hull. He regretted that the Stoneferry project was intended to supplant Springhead; he would like it in addition to Springhead. Horner persisted and during April, 1844, organised a petition to be presented to the Town Council requesting that the Derringham Springs, works and present supply of water may be continued as heretofore. This petition was presented with 2,576 signatures, including those of many highly-respected persons, some of them ladies. Dr. Alderson did not sign it, being on the Council, but agreed with it. The Mayor, in the Council meeting of 5 June, 1844, said that as far as he knew there was no intention of parting with the present waterworks. Thompson told the Council that choice of supply was utterly impracticable because of expense, but those who wanted Derringham water might have the option of carting it. This gave great satisfaction to Dr. Alderson who, minutes before, had been quite put out at the suggestion (corroborated by several) that his late father John Alderson, M.D., Hon. Physician to the Infirmary, had been an early supporter of the river as the source of the town's supply.

Nature then seemed to play her part in the controversy: *Eastern Counties Herald,* 20 June, 1844, 'The Derringham Springs. After 13 weeks of uninterrupted drought, these springs exhibit, as yet, no symptoms of exhaustion . . . Does not this fact prove their competency to furnish the town with abundance of the pure element and at the same time demonstrate that the subterranean reservoir is independent of casual supplies?'

1844, EXPERT EVIDENCE

The Health of Towns Commission continued its enquiries during 1844 and the questions put to David Thorp, the Borough Surveyor, were printed in the papers. His replies give detailed insight into the working of the water supply system as well as the related topics of drainage and sewerage.

'Do you not consider that an apparatus in the nature of a water closet may be made so cheap as to be generally applicable to labourers' tenements?' Thorp had no doubt of it, for he had had experience at the Hull Gaol, where he had constructed water closets with iron soil pans and pipes. They had no regular supply of water, 'only such water as may be put in from time to time'; in fact they were used like sinks. 'But,' said Thorp, 'it would be a proper improvement to have regular supplies of water and then the apparatus would work completely.' Even so, he assured the Commissioners that in the present circumstances they were sufficient to prevent the smell coming into the room from the drain.

The Commissioners told him that water cocks could be made which would admit the flow of a given quantity of water and no more; and where the water could be kept on the premises at high pressure, it may be applied to cleanse the water closet without the expense of a water tank to give a proper head of water.

Thorp agreed that these arrangements would be invaluable additions to the public health. Assuming these appliances could be made on a large scale, said the Commissioners, did Thorp think they could be put into labourers' tenements and trapped communication made to the public sewers at a cost of less than £2 per annum per tenement, or, if levied as rent at 2/- (10p) per tenement per year, that is, less than ½d a week? Thorp agreed that it could be done, but felt it must be done by public authority, as, he said, some people would use the apparatus as a sink, some might throw ashes in it, but the majority would use it properly.

He told the Commissioners that if there was a proper water supply, the drains would be kept cleansed, just as the drains flushed by the docks water were kept clean. The drains at the Gaol used to be flushed out about once every two years, but now they are cleansed once a month, cases of fever are unknown, he said.

The Commissioners also told Thorp about Philadelphia and Huddersfield, both places where the water was kept at high pressure. This allowed hosing of streets, windows and fronts of houses once a week; street cleaning being at a cost of about 7/- (35p) per mile for a 60ft. wide street. Thorp had doubts about the feasibility of this in Hull because of the small size of the paving stones and the extra cost of raising a head of water by steam power.

The danger of poisoning from lead piping was next discussed and Thorp said he thought there was little danger if the storage tanks were kept full, but when leaves, etc. got in and the atmosphere was allowed to act on the contained waters there was danger because 'then the lead begins to decompose.' He did not see why cast iron pipes should not be used and they would be about half the cost of the lead ones.

The Commissioners estimated the extra cost of keeping water on at a high pressure night and day either by an elevated reservoir or the constant use of a steam engine, to be about 1/6 (7½p) per tenement per year. Didn't Thorp think such a charge, less than a farthing a week 'would be an economy of insurances even for a labourer's tenement?' 'Thorp: I have no doubt that if such arrangements were made, a considerable proportion of the houses in Hull would have water laid on every landing in the house.' The use of taps or cocks which only allowed the water to run when the hand pressed on them, was described to Thorp, who said they had a cock of this kind in the town, furnished by Wicksteed, which might be more extensively used. 'The fact is that the greatest waste we experience is in the present system of having the water on occasionally and generally off; the careless people finding the water does not run, leave the tap open; and when the water does come on, it runs away for hours when they are not up or when they are out. This is a constant source of waste. We are obliged to threaten these people to cut off the water, but the waste continues from this very circumstance. I believe that keeping the pipes constantly full would be a great saving of water.' The Commissioners estimated the cost per tenement of always keeping water in houses at high pressure plus the cost of the cleansing apparatus and of house and street drain could be somewhere in the region of 2½d (1p) per week per tenement.

As all this was faithfully recorded in the press, the reading public, especially those disposed to stand against the Town Council's decisions, were able to store up ammunition for a further controversy that would soon arise, that of the Constant versus Intermittent Supply.

Dr. Thomas Clark, Marischal Professor of Chemistry at the University of Aberdeen, was questioned about the quality of the water. He was the originator of Clark's process (1841) by which a calculated quantity of slaked lime added to temporarily hard water (like that from the springs) precipitates the soluble calcium bicarbonate as insoluble calcium carbonate or chalk. The water thus softened, may be separated off. (This process was in use in a small way at the Bankside gasworks in the 1960s). Clark believed that if there were a choice in a district, the softer water should always be preferred, as there was less wear and tear on clothes, less soda need be used to soften the water and, of course, less of the heavily-taxed soap would be used. In Hull's case, he would have had the river water for washing and the springs for drinking, but nobody reminded him of the extra cost a dual system would entail.

Clark also said that too much weight was given to the presence of organic, especially animal, matter in natural waters, as the water is changed by the action of air. 'Water should be like Caesar's wife – unsuspected,' he said, for if it was offensive, people would drink less of it, which was not good for the health, and also intemperance would be encouraged.

1844, WATER SHORTAGE

In late August, 1844, two months after the *Eastern Counties Herald* was commenting on the springs' ability to provide an abundance of water, even after the long Spring drought, the story changed dramatically. There was an alarm about the shortage of water, passers-by noticed only too clearly the shallowness of the water in the Spring Ditch and the level in the reservoir had never been so low. On 28 August the reservoir was 3ft. 1½ins. deep in the morning, but only 1ft. 5ins. by evening. Apprehension was not only on account of there not being enough for a normal supply, but should a fire break out, the consequences could be grave. There *had* been a fire the previous day at Blaydes Staithe in which £10,000 of damage was done. This was near the river and action had been prompt, but had it not been so, the town might have been burnt down, said the *Herald* report.

On 29 August, 24,000 gallons were to be pumped up from the chalk as an emergency measure to increase supplies. It would be hard water, of course, commented the *Herald* with disfavour, hoping such a measure need not be continued for long.

On 5 September, purchase of more land from Mr. Breeding was decided upon by the Waterworks Committee, after a suggestion by Mr. Wicksteed to improve the proposed plant, following a similar improvement in the Metropolitan works, to its filtration system.

During the second week of September more than 30 'navigators' were employed to deepen the Spring Ditch, even working on the Sunday. 'The Spring Bank is now covered with the mud which they have excavated to a depth of nine inches to one foot from the reservoir to Wold Carr Bridge.'

Spring Bank here means literally the bank of the spring ditch, now Spring Bank West. On the evening of 31 August there was only eleven inches depth of water in the reservoir, even though the town supply had been restricted by turning off the mains in each district every day, half an hour within the usual time. A clear increase in the depth of the ditch by the navvies produced only 3ft 2ins. depth of water in the reservoir, little more than on the morning of the fire. When the springs were in full flow, there would be 5ft. 6ins. of water in the reservoir, but on Monday evening, 8 September, 1844, it was only 2ft. 4ins. deep. It was feared that the shortage would continue until the wet weather set in.

The drought had been nationwide, giving rise to some piteous circumstances, none more so than in those districts where the poor farmers and cowkeepers had been under the painful necessity of sending milk to market in its natural state as they had not enough water to thin it down.

The scarcity of water in Hull continued through the exceptionally dry and mild winter of 1844-5. The papers reported on the situation from time to time, especially when the shortage led to drama. The Boxing Day issue of the *Eastern Counties Herald* carried the following story:

'On Tuesday last, Mrs. Mary Mitchell, of Edward's Sq., Union Sq., New George Street, appeared before the Magistrates, Messrs Cookman, Firbank and Barkworth, to answer a summons charging her with throwing half a bucket of water upon her neighbour, William Scott, of Union Sq. It appeared that whenever the tap in Union Sq. is running, no water will flow from the one in Edward's Sq., the inhabitants of which consequently resort to what they call the main tap in Union Sq., where the inhabitants feel annoyed at having to take longer turns than they would have to do if they alone used the main tap; and to compel the Edward's Sq. people to desist from the main tap provoked this assault by forcibly removing the defendant's bucket. The Magistrates decided that Scott, who so removed the bucket when taking a regular turn, was in first fault, advised him to be more neighbourly during the scarcity of water and ordered him to pay for the summons.'

1845, THE STONEFERRY WORKS . . .

As though to reassure its readers that there really would be a supply adequate to the town's needs in the near future, the *Eastern Counties Herald* carried, on 20 March, 1845, a long and detailed description of the Stoneferry works in their incomplete state and how they would appear when finished. The 'unostentatious ceremony' of laying the foundation plate of the standpipe tower, performed by Ald. Thompson, in presence of Mr. Wicksteed and a few members of the Town Council was now eleven months past. Ald. Thompson had said on that occasion, that he was confident the day would come when these works would be regarded as one of the most useful and important additions which had been made in this town in this active stage of its history.

The report continued, '. . . last April the site of the new works presented to the eye little else besides long banks of newly-excavated earth on either side of the intended reservoirs, nor is their present appearance more prepossessing. Hereafter these banks will be clothed with verdure and kept in good order. With the buildings upon the site, greater progress has been made. Where in April last were seen sundry pits for the reception of the foundations of the intended tower and column, stand now the lofty buildings of white brick, which may be seen for a considerable distance around, and have a bright and cheerful look. The majestic stand pipe tower has attained (with the exception of the ornamental cap) its full height of 160ft., whilst the engine house – which is no less than 50ft. and of fair proportions – being faced with pilasters 8ft. apart, headed by semicircular arches and crowned

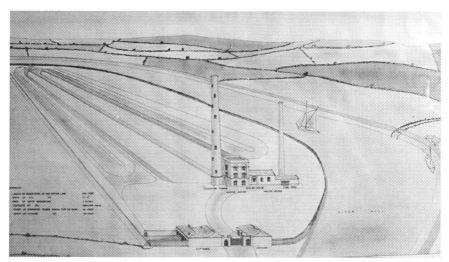

Wicksteed's original plan of the Stoneferry works as seen at Yorkshire Water's Museum, Springhead.

Photograph: Mr. A. McTurk. By kind permission of the Senior Keeper, Mr. D. W. Atkinson

by a neat cornice, stands at its feet, one might imagine purposely to set off the gigantic proportions of the tower. Contiguous is the boiler house, a smaller building in the same style, with its chimney of 120ft. crowned by a cap of the same moulding as that of the Eddystone lighthouse. By the bye, the loftier tower erected for the stand pipe is not very dissimilar to one of those maritime beacons, being lighted at regular intervals by 16 windows with Roman heads.'

The boiler house machinery from Messrs Witham of Kirkstall Road, Leeds, was in course of installation and Mr. Aird, the London contractor, was making good progress in laying throughout the town the 3,000 tons of iron pipes supplied by the Brymbo Co. 'at a price, considering the recent advance in the market, the town has every reason to be satisfied with.' In the financial sense, at least, 'the execution of the new works was one of those things of which it might be said 'If 'twere done, then 'tis well it were done quickly.' Had not the Town Council urged forward the measure as they did two years ago, the loss of one session in Parliament would have entailed a sacrifice of many thousands of pounds in the article of iron mains alone.'

Pipe laying had been facilitated by the mild winter; only a severe frost the Friday before the publication of this article had interrupted the work, and was the start of a frosty spell which delayed the work still further.

Wicksteed had produced plans for filtering the water and, although the Town Council did not think it necessary, they had agreed to the filtration system 'out of deference to what they believe to be a popular prejudice.'. The article ended with a plea that the water supply should be constant and not intermittent and with another plea to abolish the stand cocks in various places for supplying poorer people and instead to carry the pipes into every house.

Following the description as it continued in the paper's next issue, the readers would learn that all the excavation for the reservoirs and the swimming bath to be incorporated into the complex was completed. The size of the reservoirs at the waterline was 935ft. by 173ft. and the capacity of both 5,844,743 gallons. The 60ft. by 30ft. swimming bath was to be covered by a building containing dressing rooms for ladies and stalls with benches for the men, 'We need not add that the apartments will be entirely distinct.' The temperature would be 60°-70°F; in fact it was to use the 'waste' from the boiler that the swimming bath was built, following a late resolution from Ald. Thompson the previous November.

1845, THE SANATORY REPORT ON THE TOWN OF HULL BY JAMES SMITH OF DEANSTON

This was received in early April, 1845; the Stoneferry works were well on their way to completion and here were definitive arguments on public health.

However, the Report did not foresee any problem connected with the quality of the Stoneferry water, but rejoiced implicitly in the greatly increased quantity and all that was possible with an ample supply.

The report gave statistics and a general picture first. In 1841 the population of Hull was 41,130 in 8,136 houses – figures that do not tally with those used by Wicksteed. The average age of all who died was 28 years: of adults 52 years 5 months, showing the high rate of infant and juvenile mortality. The proportion of deaths under five years to total deaths was 46%, or, nearly half those who died were infants.

'The low-lying nature of the area gave a general surface of about six feet above high tides, which rise to a height of about 18ft. from low water at spring tides which are the highest.' Despite the crowded nature of the high and narrow houses in the main streets, intersected by numerous alleys through the blocks of buildings, the report commented on how pleasing it was 'after having passed through a long, narrow and filthy passage to find yourself all at once in a court of 20-40ft. square or oblong with a paved area washed as clean as the deck of a ship . . .'

The main streets in the town had covered sewers down the middle and the use of dock water entering with considerable force by means of traps or sluices, kept them in good condition. But the surface and sewage water was led to these mains in open channels and sewer gases were driven into the open. Only three of the gulley-holes or sinks were trapped to prevent the stench from rising. The paving and macadamising in old streets where there were no sewers, were either totally lacking or broken and rough so that there were filthy stagnant pools in the hollows 'and the nuisance is in many cases greatly aggravated by the slop water and filth thrown from the doors and windows of the houses.' Some of the better class of houses, built more recently, had closed sewers from each house communicating with a main sewer, but it then discharged into an open ditch. Because of the flat land there was little fall for the sewage so the closed sewers had to be opened to be cleansed and fever frequently followed opening these sewers in a neighbourhood. The prison in Sculcoates, however, was much healthier since the installation of trapped water closets.

A graphic account is given of the muck-gathering procedure. Hull was remarkable in that muck was taken from the houses regularly, each privy and ash-bin being cleared every second day, at least. This was an advantage, but was due entirely to the muck-merchants wishing to collect as much as possible for the money it represented. Unfortunately, these merchants, although taking it from individual houses regularly, then deposited it in large heaps in their muckyards here and there in the town where it constituted an even bigger nuisance. The muck and dung were sorted and mixed to suit the customers and then shipped out to farmers in Lincolnshire and elsewhere to buy at 3/- (15p) per ton. After paying assistants' wages and the cost of keeping a horse, the muck merchant made about 14/- (70p) a week, which compared favourably with the 9/- (45p) weekly wage of the street cleaners or scavengers employed by the Myton and Sculcoates Commissioners in their various areas of administration.

'The supply of water is deficient,' stated Smith's report, 'but an Act has just been obtained for procuring a greater supply; much contention has existed between two parties in the attaining of the Act, the one contending for having the water from one source, and the other from another. It is now believed, by persons competent to judge, that the source whence the water is being procured will afford water of good quality and there will be no difficulty in carrying the water into every house and keeping a constant supply at high pressure,'

Oh dear! Were these words used provocatively to urge the Council to take that line, or had the Commissioners formed the opinion, during their questioning, that a constant high pressure supply in every house was the intention of the Council as part of the Stoneferry scheme?

James Smith noted the highly political atmosphere – even going to see the poorer districts was 'taking a side'. That the supply of water needed to be increased was obvious to him, but he found that the extension of supply was a party measure, bitterly opposed by many respectable persons.

'The supply of water was intermittent. The advantages of a constant supply of water in the reduction of tenants' expenses of tanks, in a readier means afforded for private baths and for cleansing the streets, had not been seen nor provided for.' This opinion from the report was echoed in a wider way by the *Daily News*, when reporting the spread of cholera across the continent of Europe in September, 1852 : 'People are so accustomed to the thought of the necessity of disease and death, that to prevent them on a large scale seldom enters their calculations.'

The *Herald* leader at the time of Smith's report commented that 'the loss of productive labour in Hull and Sculcoates in the 1841 mortality figures amounts to £106,402, yet if any political party proposed they spend £100,000 in any one year in improved sanitary arrangements in this town and to tax the inhabitants, what an outcry there would be!'

1845, STILL LESS WATER

The summer months before the opening of the Stoneferry works must have been pretty miserable, as water was available every other weekday only, the hours of service depending on the depths at the reservoir. As the poor could not afford proper cisterns and used small open kitchen vessels instead, the stored water became 'heated and absorbed vitiated air' which 'renders it unpleasant as a beverage and induces the tenant to other injurious modes of allaying thirst.'

According to the *Herald* (17 April, 1845), the average consumption of water for a cottage should be about 40 – 50 gallons a day. The blame for the shortage was not laid at the Town Council's door, it was the drought and anyway the Council was now in Wicksteed's hands, a man who had before this been employed by private companies, supplying water as a commercial speculation. Wicksteed regarded a constant supply as a waste of water. Reporting that Manchester Corporation was about to support continuous water at high pressure, the *Herald* said, 'Let the *present* generation participate in its advantages and enjoy the more than abundant supply which the reservoirs at Stoneferry are capable of affording.'

On 9 April, 1845, at the Police Court, Mr. Jalland called attention of Ald. Thompson to the present scanty supply. Jalland had sent a cart (with permission to do so) to be filled at the ditch at the Botanic Waterworks with water for brewing purposes, but the ditch was too shallow to be able to get any. Thompson said after the recent frost the supply had diminished to as low as it ever had been. 24,000 galls were pumped up daily 'out of the solid rock . . . yet here are people who turn the taps on overnight and the water thus runs for one to two hours to the drains.' Thompson advised Jalland to sent the cart at the time of low water to the pump at North Bridge 'where he would get water as good as any in the Spring Ditch.'

From the *Herald*, 31 July, 1845 : 'The new Waterworks, will, we believe be in operation in the course of a few days. Our townsmen will hear the announcement with pleasure. Thick, hard and inodorous – not to say stinking – [*mal*odorous, surely!] 'the water supplied of late from the Spring Ditch has been unfit for domestic use and any change can hardly be for the worse. We have already stated that the water from the River Hull will be filtered; if we are rightly informed, the system of filtering is exceedingly effective and will give us a clear, cool and colourless beverage, the value of which, by contrast, we shall all be prepared to appreciate.'

TOO LATE?

The ground swell of public opinion on the desirability of a constant supply of water, started late in the proceedings, now began to gather momentum, fed by ideas gleaned from Smith's official report and elsewhere. The *Herald* begged the Council to take heed of Dr. Playfair's report on Lancashire, where Playfair had been Commissioner, with the words, 'NO DOUBT A HIGH PRESSURE, CONSTANT SUPPLY WILL BECOME THE NORM, SO WHY NOT DO IT NOW AT LESS COST OR WHEN AN ACT OF PARLIAMENT FORCES IT ON THE COUNCIL?"

In May, 1845, a meeting of Liberal electors of Myton Ward petitioned the Town Council to furnish a constant supply of water. Their argument was based on the moral value of cleanliness, and on the unwholesomeness of water standing in containers. They cited other towns, e.g. Nottingham, where water rents went up a penny a week, but people paid cheerfully because of the benefits. The petition was sent to the Council even though Thompson had told one of the Myton Liberals that it was too late to change anything as it would mean different pipage, much of which was already laid.

The *Herald* at this time referred to other places where there were constant high pressure supplies. For example, in Ayr, Greenock and Paisley such supplies cost a family of five 2/2, 2/6 and 2/9 a year respectively (i.e. 11p, 12½p and 14p). A report from Nottingham showed that it was less expensive to pump 24 hours a day than to employ extra turncocks and do extra repairs to valves, etc. The manager of the waterworks at Preston (Lancs.) said, 'I think the constant supply is a way of saving water.'

The petition from the South Myton group was read at the Council meeting in mid-June. The names included some surgeons and chemists. Although the accompanying letter was mild and complimentary, Ald. Thompson recognised among the signatories a few whose names had appeared on previous documents intended to annoy the Waterworks Committee. The memorialists had been led to believe that they would have a constant supply of water. 'Thompson could not see how they came to this notion, as in all the reports of the Waterworks Committee and especially that of 4 April, 1843, *THE SUPPLY INTENDED TO BE GIVEN WAS DISTINCTLY STATED TO BE AN ABUNDANT DAILY SUPPLY*. (Thompson was correct in this). 'That is what we intend to give', continued he. 'Mr. Palmer: 'A what?' Alderman Thompson: 'An abundant daily supply.' Mr. Palmer: 'Why, that is what they are asking for, is it not?' Alderman Thompson: 'No, they ask for a constant supply and I believe there are a number of people who do not know the difference between a daily and a constant supply. It was never intended to give them a constant supply or a supply on alternate days, but it was intended to serve them daily (hear, hear) and that each part of the borough should have an equally abundant supply with those near the works."

Ald. Thompson: '. . .the great object of the Committee was to give the best supply to those who were most in need of it; they would have done this to a greater extent had they not been crippled by such stringent clauses as that of the water closets, for which they had to thank Mr. Gresham and men like him, for whose convenience the public have to pay, whilst the parties themselves are able to pay or ought . . .' The Mayor hoped that every builder of a house would take notice, for he thought that one of the greatest comforts in a house was a water closet and when they were told by Mr. Thompson they would have nothing to pay for the water, he thought every man would be to blame who did not have one. (Laughter)'

The Myton Liberals were to be told that their petition had had serious consideration of the Waterworks Committee, but a constant supply was impracticable.

The *Herald* commented on this meeting that in the confusion of usage of the words 'daily', 'equal' and 'abundant'. 'many worthy councillors must have gone home under the impression that the water would be turned on to every house in town from 6 a.m. to 6 p.m. and that the service pipes would only be used at night to secure the highest available pressure in case of fire! A little reflection, however, will show that such an arrangement. . .would be an entire concession of the practicality of a constant supply.' It seemed that for the town to have a daily supply meant nothing more than that one district would have water in the mornings another in the afternoon, a third in the evening.

In the *Herald*'s opinion, Wicksteed looked too much to the mechanics and too little at the sanitary advantages. 'It matters not that a woman waits 25 instead of 15 seconds to fill a kettle, more important that the water is there when she wants it.' And, further, 'The constant supply of a cool, clear, refreshing and filtered water in the pipes would prove a more powerful incentive to temperance among the poor than any other single measure.'

The same leader-writer tried to be fair, however, when he stated, 'The reports of the Health of Towns Commissioners have let in a flood of light upon the question of a constant supply of water and it is no disparagement to the Waterworks Committee and their Engineer to say that they, like the rest of the world, were not fully aware of its vast importance in a moral, social and religious point of view.'

So the days before the opening of the Stoneferry Waterworks went by:

THE *EASTERN COUNTIES HERALD* in sarcastic vein about the handsome tower with stone cornice resembling the Eddystone light-house – 'It is right that our readers should know that it has been built by Mr. Wicksteed as a great coat for his stand-pipe, expressly in order to enable him to 'shut up shop' at the works and send the engine-man home to bed at reasonable hours.' (i.e. not a constant supply)

THE SEWAGE, DRAINAGE, etc. OF TOWNS BILL of mid-August – 'A supply of water for domestic purposes is to be taken to include a supply for family consumption including baths and for the cleansing of house drains, privies and water closets.'

EDWIN CHADWICK in a lecture to the College of Civil Engineers (reported 21 August) – '. . . large masses of capital are expended in works for the distribution of water in our towns without a competent knowledge of hydraulics' and money spent on an intermittent water supply 'is an ill-advised and lavish expenditure.'

HERE IS THE WATER !

In late August, 1845, the papers announced that the Stoneferry Waterworks were completed and the whole borough would be supplied in a few days. The water was much softer than the spring water and therefore much better for domestic use. The borough had outgrown the springs' supply and credit was due to the New Waterworks Committee – Ald. Thompson (chairman), Ald. Ayre, Ald. Atkinson, Mr. J. Blundell and Mr. T. A. Wilkinson – for the provision of this new and ample supply. Granted it was intermittent, but it was provided daily to every house.

This was not quite true. A Public Notice of 19 June, 1845, told 'persons intending to be supplied with water when the new Waterworks comes into operation' that they must give notice if they wanted pipes laid. This clearly would not include everybody, nor every house.

Hull was one of the few places where the water undertaking was in the hands of the Corporation; the revenue was to be £2,600 paid into the Borough Fund and the rest used to pay off loans incurred in the works. It was surprising to find that the original estimate of £60,000 had not been reached; in fact, a rare occurrence in works of this kind, £6,000 had been saved.

To celebrate there was the usual public dinner. 'To this there can be no objection,' said the *Herald* a few days later, 'but we trust the Waterworks Committee will not indulge in any undue elation on the occasion . . . Let us hope that at the festivities on Monday, some invisible genius of humility will whisper in the ears of each member of the municipal senate, 'Remember that your work is only half complete!' '

The dinner was, however, 'a more gratifying commingling of parties than has for a long period been witnessed in this town'. The opposition to the transition from Springhead to Stoneferry had largely (but not totally) been from the Conservative party, 'who now see reason to believe they were wrong.'

'With respect to the mode of supply, opinions differ' stated the *Herald*, 'but HERE IS THE WATER'. The works had the capability of supplying twice the present amount on either a constant or an intermittent system.

Ald Thompson, who had been Chairman of the Waterworks Committee since 1842, the beginning of its more active phase, said that at the start of 1843, the average supply per house was 53 gallons per day, or 9 gallons per individual (obviously reckoning about 5 or 6 people per house). By 1844 there were more people and less spring water, so that the average per house dropped to only 20 gallons and many who paid water rents were unable to get water at all. Fickle Nature was at work again, for in the very week before the Stoneferry plant opened, heavy rain filled the Botanic reservoir, after it had been as low as Ald. Thompson could remember. The water supplied was therefore muddy; it would take a few days to clear and become replaced by the filtered river water. 'The average would be about 100 gallons per house per day and indeed the Government would very probably bring in a Bill to compel everyone to have water.'

Mr. Jalland observed that people must have been anticipating the new works for charges for drunkenness at the Police court had greatly fallen off during the past year. Perhaps the various temperance societies active in the town would take the credit for themselves.

Ald. Atkinson proposed a toast to the Mayor and Corporation of Beverley, commenting upon the 'kindly feeling shewn by that town to this . . . by the cleansing of the Beck and the construction of a reservoir to receive any foul deposit from the sewerage and prevent its entering the River Hull, from which our water in future is to be derived.' In his response, Ald. Sandwith of Beverley spoke of 'the most absurd and exaggerated statements. . . respecting the quality of the water from the river.' He did not regret these statements had been made because it led to a closer examination of the water. The reservoir mentioned had been 'found' – 4ft. deep and 40 yds long – near the Beck. It had never been cleared out and was useless, so another large tank, the length of a street and a stone's throw away had been added, so that the sewage water may there deposit solid matter, *AND I SAY IT IS ALMOST IMPOSSIBLE THAT ANY IMPURE SUBSTANCE FROM THE SEWERAGE SHOULD ENTER THIS RESERVOIR AND I DEFY ANY MAN TO PROVE THAT THE SMALLEST QUANTITY OF FILTH CAN ENTER YOUR RESERVOIR.'*

Although unhappy about the intermittent supply, the *Herald* reporter eulogised the new works in his description. Near the entrance were the two houses for the resident engineer and the matron of the baths; there was also an accounts office. The baths were to the left of these and the two reservoirs were separated by a handsome gravel walk. Each reservoir was over 300 yards long, the western one being wider than the east. Water entered the west reservoir from the river through a basin provided with booms to keep out weeds and floating debris, or, in Wicksteed's words 'all scum, flax,

River Hull at Stoneferry. The Waterworks were on the left bank.
Photograph: 1995.

flue or other floating matters.' (Flue was fluff or down). From the north end of the large reservoir, the water flowed slowly to its other end, depositing impurities. A culvert then led the water to the east reservoir where it passed through layers of gravel and fine white sand to filter it and there were also 12 airbrick chimneys in the middle of this reservoir to admit air into the water. From the east reservoir a culvert went under the engine house and the water was forced up one of the 24 inch diameter pipes in the tower, then came down the other pipe so as to provide gravity feed for distribution.

The engines were of the Cornish variety, a species which had been confidently predicted (so reported the *Athenaeum* in April, 1844) to be unable to thrive or produce to the same amount and perfection anywhere else as it had done in its native soil. Wicksteed had published a book illustrated with the Cornish and Boulton and Watt engines at the East London Waterworks – 'the first engines transplanted out of Cornwall'. Their appearance in Hull was something of a novelty in itself. Providing 64 h.p. each, the engines between them could raise nearly 500 cu.ft. of water a minute. Only one engine was in use at the start of the operation, the other in reserve. It was expected that only one engine would be needed for years to come.

The *Herald* reporter had climbed inside to the top of the standpipe tower on wooden ladders constructed in 30ft. stages. At the top stage the rush of water in the pipes could be heard and it was hard to climb because the tower narrowed. But, oh the view when he reached the top!

From 160ft. above the flat countryside he could see Beverley Minster, the hills beyond Driffield, the hills of Lincolnshire, the high ground of Hessle and Swanland, the sea coast and the German Ocean, visible for miles on a clear day, even to Spurn Point. The view was disfigured by the tall chimneys of various manufactories of Sculcoates and Drypool, belching black smoke. 'Immediately beneath the spectator is the tiny River Hull like a silver thread stretching away north and south, and the reservoirs, the latter looking like lakes of molten silver when the sun's rays are on them, and with their gravel border, looking brightness and clearness themselves.'

Various devices were incorporated to try and ensure the smooth working of a plant contiguous to a tidal river. There were flaps between the balance gates and the reservoirs to prevent water flowing back again when the level of low water was lower than the level in the reservoir. A bank to the east of the filtering reservoir was sufficiently high to prevent the river overflowing into the reservoir at the highest tides. Fine wire gratings in a double row were fixed across the entrance to the reservoirs and also between the reservoirs and the engine-wells. These would remove fine matter and could be taken out for cleaning.

The METHOD OF OPERATION was to take in water at the period of low tide, so that the salty water of the Humber was supposedly excluded and the reservoirs would take in the fresh coming down from the higher reaches of the River Hull. To ensure that water was taken in at this time

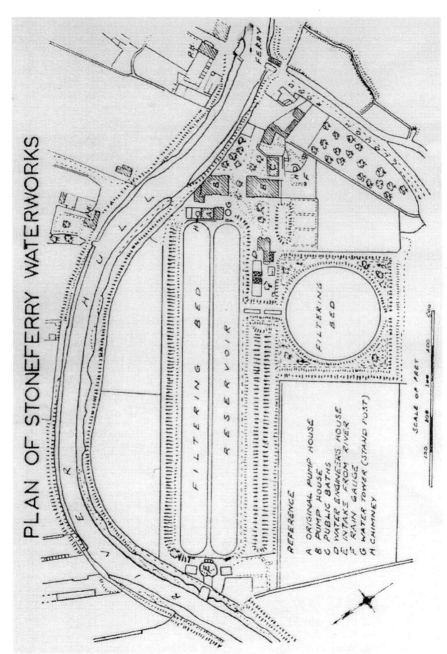

Plan of the Stoneferry Works.

From Kingston upon Hull Corporation Water Department booklet, 1970

only, the sluices at the entrance basin had balance gates so constructed that when the water in the river had fallen to a proper level, the falling of a float 6 inches in the entrance basin would cause the gate to rise 3 feet; upon the river again rising 6 inches, the gates would be shut close and remain so until the next low water. The removal of visible filth was to be ensured by the various booms and filtering devices already described, but there seemed to be no conception that there could be harmful invisible material in the filtered water.

The amenities of the public baths were mentioned in the descriptive article when the works were first opened, but the reporter went to see for himself the following March:

'We visited the other day the public baths at the New Waterworks, Stoneferry, and found the quality and temperature of the tepid swimming bath all that could be wished. The latter was at nearly 80 degrees. A plunge at any time of the year in water of that temperature is refreshing, and we are glad to find that throughout the winter these baths have been daily used to a considerable extent. In fact, notwithstanding their distance of from two or three miles from the heart of the town, they have become, we believe, the most frequented place of ablution for our vast population of from 70,000 to 100,000 inhabitants. As the warmth of the weather increases, so do *(sic)* the number of bathers, and we calculate for these baths an extraordinary business during the ensuing summer. For a penny you have the use of a towel and a screened dressing-box; for sixpence, you have a private bath. The necessity of such an establishment became manifest when the railway destroyed the baths on the west of the town. It is increased now that the working classes are excluded from the garrison ground behind the Citadel. It is much to be wished that another cheap bathing establishment should be opened nearer the town, and the Corporation will confer a vast boon upon the public whenever they open the Old Waterworks for that purpose . . .'

So the Stoneferry Waterworks, Alderman Thompson's pride and joy, came into being.

There were a few early troubles, especially the bursting of water mains, but, from the way these items of news reached the public via accounts of Town Council meetings, this was not considered to be a major problems as by November, 1845, *only* eleven pipes had burst in 30 miles. Sometimes it provided free entertainment, as on 2 October, 1845:-

'Bursting of another main. On Tuesday evening about 8 o'clock a main water pipe burst in Prospect Street opposite Baker Street forcing the water up to the garret windows of adjoining houses and deluging the road. For about half an hour the inhabitants were gratified by the playing of this magnificent fountain, when the water was turned off by the Company's servant, and the road ceased to send forth its liquid stream, to the infinite regret of the surrounding throng, who had considerably been endeavouring to plug up the breach with caps, handkerchiefs, stones, etc.'

Some repairs to the engines were needed in the spring of 1846, which prevented them working at night, but by the end of April this had been remedied.

Mr. Robert A. Marillier was appointed resident engineer and the 'esteemed' Mr. Collins, who had been Supervisor during the construction, left Hull at the beginning of May, 1846.

'The state and prospect of the works appear to be satisfactory to the New Waterworks Committee and likely to afford an abundant supply of water to all.' That appeared in the *Herald* on 30 April, 1846. In the same issue was the headline:

APPROACH OF THE ASIATIC CHOLERA

Cholera was 'carrying off thousands' in some European towns. Already reported in Germany, it was predicted to arrive in England in the heat of the summer. The crowded, badly-ventilated tenements in the Pottery (i.e. the St. James Street, Hessle Road, area) and bad drainage in Holderness and Sculcoates wards 'are among the most efficient aides such a scourge can have.' As the Health of Towns Commissioners had said in 1843, 'The supply of water is so intimately connected with an efficient system of drainage, that we shall now be compelled to mix up the two questions.' They did not consider a supply of water sufficient for domestic and culinary purposes with a small overplus for washing down the courtyards or the foot pavement now and then, an abundant supply. They would make clean water not only cleanse drains, but act as the scavenger in the streets, and supplant the scraper and the broom. The Hull Town Council had not as yet come to the same way of thinking.

So inevitable was the onward march of the cholera that it was not a matter of *if* it would arrive, but *when* it would come. Trade between Hull and European ports, especially Hamburg, had been flourishing (Hull was by this time the third port in foreign trade) and it seemed likely that this would be the means of entry of the epidemic.

Local newspaper reports were few in number, but sinister in content:

20 July, 1848, St. Petersburg, Moscow, the Polish-Lithuanian border, Moldavia.

12 August, 1848, Cairo, Russia, Galicia, Sweden.

14 September, 1848, 'We apprehend that cholera is taking the same route as it did in 1832.'

28 September, 1848, 'Cases of Cholera at Hull.' There were three deaths from cholera on board the barque Pallas of Stettin, which for months had been in the Old Dock with the carpenter on board as caretaker while the master and crew went back home. They had returned the previous Friday on a steamer from Hamburg where cholera had prevailed for some weeks.

By Monday three were dead and another man ill, but recovering. A police constable was set to guard the vessel so that there should be no ship to shore communication, even though Dr. Ayre said that cholera was not contagious.

MEANWHILE . . .

After the opening of the Stoneferry Waterworks, some effort was made in Hull to improve the drainage, or, more particularly, to remove the stench from the streets, as there was fear that the smells or effluvia emitted by the sewers would prove injurious to the health of the townspeople; the Whitefriargate sewer, for example, was so bad that it was 'a celebrity for its stench'.

The meeting, on 25 May, 1846, of the Myton Commissioners was but one among many in which disputes and anomalies between the different bodies came to light. In this meeting, reference was made to a drain between Waltham Street and Albion Street on the boundary between Myton and Sculcoates. Some Myton properties drained into it, but that did not give the Myton Commissioners full jurisdiction over it, nor did the Sculcoates Commissioners have full power to deal with the matter now that the drain needed covering. Difficulties like this, some resolved, some left unsolved or merely bodged, led to repeated suggestions in the meetings of the various administrative bodies that they should merge and the whole of the borough be administered by a single authority.

Upon Lord Morpeth's Contagious and Epidemic Diseases Prevention Act becoming law on 28 August, 1846, the Editor of the *Eastern Counties Herald* commented in a leading article, 'These powers, however, are fearfully deficient of what is required for the sanatory requirements of this borough.'

Examples of drains or ditches filled with stagnant filth, of the soil of cess-pools being left on the roadside after being cleaned out of the pits, of the bad state of the pavements with stagnant pools in them after disturbance due to the laying of water pipes, and other matters affecting the public health, were reported in every issue of the local papers. Among the 'filth and nastiness' were encouraging signs of improvements in certain things, as in the erection of stand-pipes in strategic places so that portable hoses may be screwed on to them in case of fire; and the experiment by the Waterworks Committee of portable hose and ladders in which the hose, within 5 minutes, was able to eject a stream of water over a five storey house and the ladders in 6 foot lengths were put together and reared up to a tall building in two minutes. Under the supervision of Mr. Thorp, the Borough Surveyor, hundreds of sink traps (or 'stink traps') had been installed but more were needed, especially in Bishop Lane. The old road surfaces of sea cobbles set in pulverised chalk and gravel were not suitable for the increasing traffic of the town and slaps forming between the cobbles were harbours for stagnant water and rotting filth. However, between 7 p.m. and 9 or 10 p.m. the turncocks opened the standpipe plugs to swill much of the dirt down the drains and householders took the opportunity to brush courts, areas and shop fronts that were within range of the standpipe water. Watering the streets by water cart was not always regularly done. Here is the *Herald* in ironic mood on the subject, 11 June, 1846: 'Strange to say, just as we were writing the last word of the last sentences a real water cart passed our office. We hail its appearance as foreshadowing the approach of rain much more surely than the fall of the barometer. We consider it as somehow or other actuated by the hidden influences like the woman who sometimes stands on top of a German clock: but there is this difference between her and the cart, for when rain is coming, she pops into a snug little shed, while the cart wanders abroad as if thoroughly reckless of the pelting it is doomed to encounter.'

Of the river water now supplied, in July, 1846, there were many complaints about its saltiness. The *Herald*'s investigative reporter found that on 22 July, two men were on duty to see the balance gates were closed before the tide had risen more than a few inches, but as one man had had only a fortnight's experience under the engineer and the other was a totally inexperienced new employee, they let the water rise four feet and thus salt water came in with the tide. The gates were supposedly self-acting, 'but do not appear exactly to answer the purpose for which they were intended; notwithstanding this defect, however, proper caution being used, it is absolutely impossible that any salt water could gain admission.' The mains were emptied on to the streets to rid them of salt water, but individual tanks and cisterns had also to be cleaned. In February, 1847, complaints were received of thick and muddy water. This was due to the turbidity of the river during rain and the simultaneous cleaning of the filter, which could no longer be deferred. Usually this was done when the river was clear, but this time the rain and therefore the muddiness happened after the filters were removed.

Another rather flowery description of the Stoneferry works appeared on 1 April, 1847, not as an April Fool's joke, but more likely inspired by spring weather encouraging a walk in that direction. The article meted out to the reading public more opinions and information on the water question and possibly revealed that the view of the *Herald* itself had shifted further in favour of Stoneferry than it had been. Or, this impression is perhaps given to a reader nowadays (like myself) because at that time the calls for retention of Springhead had apparently ceased.

Who could not look upon the works (ran the article) 'without admitting that something has at least been attempted by the ruling body of the town? The Town Council was loudly blamed for laying out some £60,000 to provide for the wants of the coming generation because it was calculated that those works would supply the need of the town for nearly 40 years without extension. How short-sighted are the keenest calculators; how owl-eyed is the clamorous public! The total number of houses supplied – supplied, did we say, we ought to have said pinched with a half or quarter supply of water – from the old waterworks was under 7,000; one fourth part of that water was brackish 'sipe', so corrosive as to prevent the water in which it was mixed from being used in steam boilers. Then the railway company sent their engines four miles to water at Hessle, where water was pumped up at the station from the chalk strata. Now, although only 20 months since Stoneferry opened, already 17,000 houses are provided with water at high pressure every day and the Railway Company is a customer to the extent of 30,000 gallons a day.' All the engines used in the construction of Victoria Dock, many breweries and large factories were taking water via Stoneferry and the demand was increasing. 'We confidently predict that before another 20 months expire it will be found advisable to increase the supply beyond the capacity of the existing engines!'

So far, so good; the added quantity of water was certainly a boon to domestic users and industry alike, but without proper drainage to cleanse the town of filth, much of the toil of keeping home and family clean, would be of no avail.

1847, A BAD YEAR

In 1847, scurvy was prevalent all over the country 'from the want of vegetable food, potatoes having failed.' Typhus was epidemic and in July showed no signs of abating. All food became scarce and dear. The *Herald* nevertheless exhorted its readers to eat more fruit and vegetables as meat and bread were not enough, '. . . but it appears that the body when duly supplied with the principles it derives from these sources (i.e. fruit and vegetables), husbands them up, and can do without the acid diet for some time . . . chemists have not hitherto explained how vegetable acids subserve nutrition.'

The Sculcoates Guardians reported in mid-September 1847, fourteen cases of typhus, including six new ones. In Mr. Liddell's buildings, Sutton Bank (the thoroughfare which continued from Holborn Street Witham, along the bank of the Sutton Drain parallel to Dansom Lane) 'some of the walls were 9ins. thick with spiders' webs.' *Eastern Counties Herald*, 4 November 1847: 'Fever. One great source of fever is the lodging houses where the idle and dissolute who spend their days in begging, congregate at nights. It is anticipated that, by sending all mendicants to gaol, where cleanliness and ventilation are attended to, the number of cases of disease will be decreased.' ('Are there no prisons?' asked Mr. Scrooge)

Outbreaks of 'fever' and of 'typhoid' were not infrequent. Typhoid and typhus were confused, the one reported as the other because clear diagnosis had not been made; dysentery and diarrhoea were common, especially in the late summer months. The consumption of stoned fruit at the time of year when plums were ripe, was a notorious cause of many upsets. In fact, the Captain and crew of the Pallas returned from Hamburg on a vessel with a cargo of plums, had eaten freely of them during the journey and '. . . it is well-known that the eating of fruit, and particularly raw fruit, and more especially stoned fruit such as plums, has a tendency to predispose the stomach and bowels for an attack of cholera,' ran the newspaper report.

As causes were not known, the remedies were diverse. *Eastern Counties Herald*, 3 June, 1847: 'Prevalence of fever in Hull. Perhaps not generally known that there is a small fund at the General Dispensary to give wine and other nourishment to those for whose cure it seems to be absolutely necessary. This fund is nearly exhausted because of fever of the Typhoid character.' There were fears that this would spread unless something were done. 'So if anyone has a bottle of Port to spare, send it to Mrs. Elizabeth Thompson, 20, Brook Street, who will dispense it under the direction of the surgeons at the Dispensary.' At least somebody understood that under-nourishment was an ally to the seriousness of the major diseases.

Bust of Dr. Joseph Ayre (1781-1860) in the Guildhall.
Photograph: Mr. A. McTurk.

DESPERATE REMEDIES

Methods of treatment for the Cholera were frequently either advertised or reported, especially during 1847 and onwards. Some actually called themselves 'cures'. The most usual treatment was the administration of opium and calomel, but unless the calomel, mercurous chloride, was free of admixture of mercuric chloride, it was so poisonous as to be a swifter killer than the cholera itself.

Joseph Ayre treated his patients with opium and calomel and he was an acknowledged authority on the disease. The Irish Central Board of Health also advocated the use of calomel and opium in its circular of instructions issued in anticipation of the arrival of the epidemic. It also advised the use of warm flannel with turpentine to be wrapped around the body; others recommended a turpentine embrocation.

Professor Liebig varied the calomel and opium treatment by using natron (soda) gruel as hot as it could be taken, followed by a little laudanum and a good dose of castor oil. If that sounded extreme, what about the 'ordinary and most convenient' Chinese treatment as described by Fr. Joseph Rizzolatti, vicar apostolic of Hong Kong? The patient's tongue was punctured in innumerable places with the point of a table knife or crystal blade to produce an abundant effusion of blood. 'Then whilst some attendants stretch the principal nerves by main force, the others give the patient severe blows on the chest, the back, the thighs and the hips until torrents of blood gush forth. When the crisis is over the patient recovers, at the cost of numerous scars and bruises and a skin as black as that of a negro.' (Quoted in the *Eastern Counties Herald*, 12 July, 1849, just as the epidemic was starting in Hull.)

There was even a report of the recovery of an 8-year-old girl from the last or collapse stage of cholera, by the application of one pole of a galvanic battery over the heart, the other pole in the stomach region. After the epidemic was over, there was a theory that the cholera (and also the potato blight of 1849) was due to the absence of ozone or electricity in the atmosphere, but this was a speculation that remained unproven.

The basic calomel and opium treatments were the most common, but the continued administration of saline liquid was claimed to have a failure rate of only 6%. Homeopaths claimed a high success rate by giving infinitesimal doses of hellebore.

ADMINISTRATIVE PREPARATIONS

On 9 November, 1847, the Town Council set up a Sanatory Committee of twelve members of the Council, to carry into effect the provisions of the Contagious and Epidemic Diseases Prevention Act. The Committee members were: Dr. Ayre, B. Boulter, H. Blundell, J. Dalton, C. A. Forrester, Dr. Gordon, D. Sandall, John Malam, Dr. Horner, Dr. Cooper, Sir W. Lowthrop, John Richardson and T. W. Palmer.

Two days later, by front page advertisement in the local press, the Corporation announced that it would accept information about nuisances under seal, that is, anonymously, so that the matter could be acted upon; but the *Herald*'s editorial commented that it would be better to appoint an Inspector of Nuisances, rather than rely on information gathered in this way.

About the same time, in response to a circular from Drs. Humphry Sandwith, Robert Craven and Henry Cooper, a meeting had been held in the library of the Infirmary in order to form the Sanatory Committee of the Medical Society of Hull and also 'to devise such measures as may seem expedient to be adopted by the profession in anticipation of the approach of the Asiatic cholera.' A useful Report was produced by this Committee, describing public health matters in Hull, district by district. It came to the conclusion that although the drains in the Old Town and parts of Myton were satisfactory, at the same time they were almost inoperative because they were not connected to the houses. The writers could not find words to express the state of the middens etc. And so on, with regard to street cleaning and other problems that were receiving both a lot of public notice and also some corrective attention from the Corporation.

The Committee for the Medical Society also made its plea for a single authority. 'No general and uniform system can be applied to the management of matters affecting public health unless it is carried out by one and the same authority, believing that clashings of local interest and jurisdiction must occur to the prejudice of the general good, wherever separate boards are entrusted with similar functions in the same town . . .'

The Town Council looked at this Report, but Dr. Ayre, as Chairman of the Corporation Sanatory Committee said it was not the duty of its members to visit places and make personal enquiries. The Surveyor was asked, but he was too busy. Palmer suggested a Health of Towns Officer at £100 p.a., but the Town Clerk said the motion could not be put as the salary could not exceed £20 p.a. Palmer contended this and there was some confusion until Cllr. Peck suggested that one of the Inspectors of Police under Chief Constable McManus, could do the work efficiently at no extra cost. This was adopted.

There *was* confusion. The arrival of the cholera seemed inevitable. The streets had recently been broken up to lay new water pipes and now there was a lot of work going on to prepare for the coming emergency or to avert the worst of it, in clearing and covering existing drains and making more effective new ones. The country was in economic recession, even monetary crisis, at the beginning of 1848 and unemployment was high. 'Immediate prospects are not the most flattering for either masters or operatives,' according to the *Herald*. Examples of families being helped by subscription revealed, for 1848-9 that a man, wife and two children had had 2 shillings (10p) per week for three months; a man, wife and four children had had no earnings for five weeks; and another man, wife and four children had earned thirty shillings (£1.50) in nine months. The expected Health of Towns Bill was not yet on the Statute Book and although the various bodies paid lip service to the idea of wanting a single authority, in practice they continued as before.

Just before Christmas, 1847, the town's Sanatory Committee addressed the inhabitants of Hull via the newspapers, hoping that people would take up the various measures that had recently been incorporated into the local bye-laws, without the Corporation having to enforce them on individuals, adding, 'It must be remembered that cholera chooses its victims by precisely the same laws as typhus and other fevers. . . and that wherever fever has prevailed, cholera, when it attacks the districts, will also be found most deadly.'

1848, THE HEALTH OF TOWNS ACT

This long-awaited measure became law in September, 1848.

Named definitely as a measure for urban areas, it excluded places of under 2,000 inhabitants over the last three Census returns; in such places public health matters had to be dealt with through the Parish Councils.

Many towns, including Hull, were of course, spreading. The *Herald* had noted the previous May, that as the town spread into the country the ditches became common sewers, exhaling a slow and subtle poison during summer and autumn. 'Owners do not deal with them, because they still see them with the nostalgic eyes of youth where they picked flowers, pelted rats and ducks, even drank the then pure water. And in the villages a stinking green pond spreads across the road. It would take little to clear it, but it has become a farmer's defence.' 'This comment followed the public meeting on 17 May, 1847, when it had been resolved to send a petition to Parliament praying that the Health of Towns Bill be made law in the current session, so as to consolidate all bodies concerned with public health, into one, a meeting at which John Gresham had voiced his belief that the Bill concerned the whole population, not just towns. He cited Hessle, where he lived 'and where there is stagnant water by the road for a quarter of a mile, the effluvia of which is enough to make a horse sick.'

The Health of Towns Act provided wide-ranging powers covering many aspects of public health. As far as water supply was concerned, it was an enabling Act: 'It shall be lawful for the Local Board to provide a constant supply at pressure of pure water for the purpose of this Act . . . If a house needs a supply and this can be done for a rate of twopence per week, this can be carried out.'

The Provisional Order for the application of the Act to Hull did not reach the Town Council until July, 1851, and thus the Local Board of Health (which was really the Town Council in different guise) was not created until that time.

Had it come into being in 1848, it is highly unlikely that it could have averted the next crisis.

1849, THE CHOLERA EPIDEMIC

In the first week of October, 1848, a week after the fatalities on board the *Pallas*, two ships in the roads were flying quarantine flags and within a few more days several ships from Hamburg were in the Humber, in quarantine. One death was reported. Dr. Sutherland, one of the Health Commissioners, was in Hull and said the town was free of cholera. Meanwhile, Dr. Ayre and Mr. Grainger, Sutherland's assistant, went to Hamburg, where they found that quarantine had been abandoned because it spread alarm, and cases of cholera were admitted to general wards of ordinary hospitals, instead of special temporary hospitals for the disease. No-one caught cholera from these patients and they got better care in the ordinary hospital because the temporary ones only attracted the lowest class of person as nurses 'whose habits and ignorance did not fit them for the job.' It was believed that to keep quarantine led to a neglect of other precautions.

Despite many cases of diarrhoea, which some thought was premonitory of cholera, the true Asiatic cholera did not appear in Hull until July, 1849. This was in a district (Fawcett Street, Little Passage Street, Middle Street) which abounded with 'those accumulations of filth which are admitted to be the chief causes of this and kindred diseases.' Most of these cases ended in death.

Dr. Ayre was appointed the physician, with W. Day, R. L. Sleight and J. B. Archbold as surgeons for cases of cholera.

There seemed to be an abatement at the end of July and this was, by some, put down to the violent thunderstorm which had split the tergallant mast of a ship in the harbour and killed some farm animals in Holderness. After this there was a rapid increase in the number of cases. The Magistrates did all they could to deal with reported nuisances on private property, but the fact that not all gratings had been fitted with the 'stink traps' meant that there were continuous, worrying smells arising from the drains.

The epidemic became the first item of editorial comment in the *Herald* and the issue of 6 September, 1849, gave the awful news that the total number of deaths within the last seven days was a number larger in proportion to the population of the town than recorded in any other provincial returns. The editorial went on, 'The Magistrates are not in earnest. For being drunk and uttering a saucy word to a policeman a man was fined five shillings (25p) and costs, but the owner of nuisances which imperil the health and lives of thousands escapes with no severe penalty.'

The use of chlorine as a deodorant and disinfectant was widespread. 'There had been a public demonstration to the Sanatory Committee and others in August, 1848, with a lecture and much discussion afterwards of Ellerman's Patent Deodoriser, the active ingredient being perchloride of iron. However, chlorine was usually derived from chloride of lime. This substance, which looks like white, chalky lumps of curd, was a common disinfectant for outside sinks and gratings until after World War II, when the generally more convenient liquids containing hypochlorous acid, came into use. Chloride of lime releases chlorine on the action of water and atmospheric carbon dioxide, but more readily on the action of sulphuric acid. A letter to the *Herald* from Ald. T. W. Palmer of Albion Street suggested that 8lbs of chloride of lime with 2lbs of sulphuric acid be put into the water carts for disinfecting the streets daily. This was carried out in Sculcoates and the presence of chlorine gas was 'distinctly felt' in Francis Street some time after the water cart had passed. The thought of the water cart going round Sculcoates, bearing the water with the chloride of lime in it, and attended by a man carrying a jug of vitriol is quite worrying, but there was no report that the man suffered any mishap during his dangerous task! Free provision of this mixture was made to the poor. Messrs. Wright and Young distributed a quantity of chloride of lime for use by the poor of High Street and the neighbourhood in the purification of their dwellings.

Barrels of tar were burned in the streets in an effort to rid the town of the pestilence though whether this was done because there might be some property in the fumes to kill the disease or whether it was merely to mask even more unpleasant smells, is not clear. It had been said during the demonstration of Ellerman's Compound, 'It could not be asserted with truth that the miasma producing disease was necessarily odorous, but its production was coincidental with putrefaction and it was not unreasonable to presume that the same chemical agent which permanently destroyed the odour of a putrefying mass, would also destroy elements that generate the noxious miasma.'

The epidemic being national and not merely local, there were reports from other parts of the country. From Bristol came another recipe for chlorine, to be used for fumigation in this instance. The gaol, bridewell, lunatic asylum and great public schools in Bristol had entrance boxes about 10ft. long through which visitors must pass. A saucerful of a 3:1 mixture of common salt and black oxide of manganese was kept inside the door and chlorine was liberated from it on the addition of vitriol. Any visitor who had been in contact with cholera patients would have the saucer moved all round him before he could enter the main building. It is not said if anyone had serious effects from chlorine poisoning or bleaching of their clothing from this process.

Many who could leave the town did so. 'Harrogate was never known to be so full of company as at present.' (20 September) Retail trade, especially food, suffered. 'Fruit and vegetables have become extremely despised. The largest and finest apples are allowed to remain till they fall from the trees; green peas are in vain hawked at 3d per peck (sold by volume, this was just over 1p for 2 gallons of peas); even potatoes, though excellent, are little used; the publicans report that only one pint of ale or porter is called for where a hundred used to be; and the choicest wines are quite neglected whilst the demand for 'the best' brandy daily increases.'

When the epidemic showed signs of abating, in late September, a large warehouse in Wincolmlee was being fitted up as a house of refuge to accommodate the inhabitants of dirty or infected localities while their houses were being 'purified' and also two hospitals had been set up, one in North Street, the other in the Groves, for destitute cholera patients. Collections were made in the churches and chapels to help the poor, for the epidemic had certainly struck at a very bad time, when the poorer part of the population was debilitated through unemployment and the lack of basic necessities.

WAS IT THE WATER?

By 1847, the Stoneferry Waterworks had dropped 'New' from the title and it was clearly recognised that the population was increasing while the demand for water was more than keeping pace with the increase. At the Town Council meeting of 9 November, 1847 (at which the Sanatory Committee was set up) Cllr. Blyth wished to put the motion, 'That in the opinion of this Council, whenever an additional supply of water shall be wanted, it will be better to take it from the old works than go to the expense of £7,000 in increasing the new works for that purpose.' On the Mayor's suggestion that this be left until after the election of next year's Waterworks Committee, Blyth withdrew the motion, but reintroduced it in October, 1848. An amendment by Mr. Jalland on this second occasion left the matter with the Waterworks Committee, already in communication with Mr. Wicksteed, who was preparing plans for the erection of a very powerful engine in addition to the two existing ones at Stoneferry. On 11 May, 1848, the *Herald* reported Wicksteed's proposals. The idea had been to work the Botanic engines in connection with the Stoneferry ones. This would require the water to be raised to 173ft. Costs were given and those people who relied solely on the papers for information would learn for the first time that although the original estimate had not been reached, nevertheless interest on loans had brought the Stoneferry expenditure up to £64,002.8s.9d. i.e. more than £4,000 over the estimated £60,000. Wicksteed showed how expensive it would be to work Botanic and Stoneferry together and so another and more powerful engine for Stoneferry was designed instead.

For more than a year nothing appeared in the press about the water supply as such. It was noted in March, 1848, that the Kingston Cotton Mills ('the largest in Britain and of course in the world') would have 1,000-2,000 employees and hot water running from the steam engine at nearly 3,000 gallons a minute in a state ready for use for washing or bathing. Since no amenity had been provided in the locality to use the water it would consequently be wasted in the river.

A few charges were made against individuals taking water without paying for it. For example, Mr. John Harrison of 7 Dock Street, was charged with having taken water for a steam engine without having entered into an agreement with the Waterworks Committee. He was originally rated at 30 shillings (£1.50) per annum for water supplied for domestic purposes and continued to pay it, although he had ceased to occupy the premises as a dwelling two years ago and by then also paid 18/- (90p) for his home. The engine in Dock Street was of 40 h.p. working one day per week for about five hours, with an estimated usage of 50 gallons each time. The waterworks charge would have been £5 for it. He paid a fine of £2 and said he would have the supply cut off as a pump on the premises would yield enough.

Some months before the cholera epidemic, the Board of Health Inspectors under James Smith, came again to survey the state of the town. Questioned specifically about the water, various doctors, councillors and others gave their opinion of it:

MR. TWINING, Surgeon: '. . . the present water was very hard and contained a large quantity of salt, and from its becoming nauseous if allowed to stand for 24 hours, he should infer there was something in it injurious to health.'

DR. DALY: did not think that the water contained more 'salt' than the generality of water, although it might contain more 'salts'. From analysis, there were only three better waters in the country.

Both Twining and Daly agreed that a constant supply would be an improvement.

DR. AYRE: 'had never heard any complaints that could lead him to suppose any inconvenience or indisposition had arisen from the use of the water.' He thought that if all the Beverley sewage went into the river, the volume of the river water was so great that no matter injurious to health could be given to the River Hull.

JOSEPH SHARP AND MR. HUTTY, collectors of water rents: 'complaints about quality and quantity are much less frequent than they used to be.'

MR. WELLS: found it necessary to use a filter, but then he had never had water so pleasant to the taste.

Mr. HOLDSWORTH: The Spring Ditch supply was totally inadequate.

MR. HENRY BLUNDELL, Councillor and colour manufacturer: gave a favourable account of the water for colour-making and for domestic use.

DR. HORNER: The water from the springs was the best round Hull and enough could be got from them.

MR. BLYTH, Councillor: Had introduced a motion to use the old works, not because of complaint about the Stoneferry water, but on account of the cost.

MR. THOMAS ABBEY, Councillor: complained of the present water not mixing well with spirits and spoiling the colour of the Hollands [gin]. He said that it would turn foul and emit a noxious smell if put into a bottle and kept for 24 hours.

MR. MARILLIER, Waterworks engineer: had kept the water for three years and it was as sweet as ever.

ALD. THOMPSON, Chairman, Waterworks Committee: 'The analysis satisfied the Commons Committee when the Bill was going through.'

DR HENRY COOPER: did not think any of the diseases prevalent in Hull were to be attributed to the water, which he believed to be quite wholesome.

MR. PEARSALL, Secretary of the Literary and Philosophical Society: the quality varied in different parts of the town, but MARILLIER said this was due to the piping and was rectified upon being reported.

During the epidemic, Dr. Horner made further moves to do something about the water supply. asked Dr. Sutherland, the Board of Health Inspector, if he thought the greater prevalence of cholera on this occasion, compared with 1832, was due to the change of water source. Sutherland was rather short and sharp in his reply, telling Horner that the Board was trying to find *IMMEDIATE* means of alleviating the present situation. The water supply was in Mr. Smith's hands; he had reported fully on the water to the Board of Health and perhaps would recommend taking from higher up the river, but that would be a long and expensive job.

Three hours were spent discussing the water situation at the Town Council meeting of 4 October, 1849, the talk initiated by Dr. Horner presenting a 2,000-signature memorial complaining of the present supply and praying the Corporation to obtain purer water. Horner was still pro-Springhead, but had come to realise that it was hardly possible that he would see a complete reversal to that source after the great expenditure at Stoneferry. Instead, he began to urge that water be taken from higher up the river, perhaps because he had learned from Sutherland that Smith was likely to recommend the same action, when his Report was eventually published. Cllr. Jacobs moved the Council wait for Smith's recommendations and this was carried.

In the same issue that the *Herald* reported the day of thanksgiving for the cessation of the cholera (15 November, 1849), during which shops were closed, 'work about the shipping' suspended and churches and chapels enjoyed full congregations at the thanksgiving services, the paper also published the REPORT ON HULL WATER. These analyses had been made in April, 1849, by Arthur Aikin, F.G.S. and Alfred Swaine Taylor, M.D., F.R.S., Professor of Chemistry at Guy's Hospital. The first sample, the unfiltered Stoneferry water, when received was a pale yellowish colour and slightly opaque due to a number of small particles mechanically diffused through it. After some time there was a brownish sediment, the supernatant liquid being 'tolerably clear and colourless'. It was free of offensive odour but had a slight taste.

The sample that had been through the Stoneferry filters was not turbid like the other, even on agitation, but it produced a slight sediment on standing for a considerable time. It had no taste and no offensive odour.

The unfiltered water contained	3.2 grains of	organic matter
	14.8 ,,	various salts
The filtered water	3 ,,	organic matter
	13 ,,	various salts
– each in one imperial gallon.		

There was more calcium carbonate after filtration, due to the material in the filter bed, but this was less than the average found in most rivers and springs.

Of sodium chloride, common salt, there were 4.0 grains to the gallon, unfiltered, and 2.5 grains to the gallon, filtered. Both samples had less sodium sulphate and more sodium chloride than the average for river and spring waters.

The quantity of salts in both the samples was enough to coat lead pipes and prevent further chemical action which would have produced soluble and poisonous lead compounds to contaminate the water. 'The chlorides are the protective influence,' was Aikin and Taylor's opinion. They thus silently condoned the amount of common salt on the grounds that it would prevent lead poisoning. The water probably could deposit enough calcium carbonate to provide the same protection.

The analyses provoked immediate reaction from 'A Water Drinker' to the Editor of the *Herald*:

> *'Your last paper contained a 'Report of the Hull Water' signed by two learned men, Mr. Aikin and Dr. Taylor, and dated 8th November. I can give you a more recent and more accurate report of the water now in use throughout the borough than any that those very scientific people, with the whole of the engineers and the water committee put together ever dared to publish . . . I question whether Mr. Aikin ever saw in any town in the kingdom such nasty dirty stuff as we have all had to drink in the last fortnight . . . By the bye, there is one witness who could be called as to the quality of the Hull water and that is Mr. Wicksteed. A dinner was given to him when he produced the first supply from the new works and it was so dirty that all at the table were ashamed of it. We have now had the supply five years and upwards, and it is as filthy, or nearly so, as on the day Mr. Wicksteed was disgusted with it and all the cheers hung fire at his public dinner. Really, the town is sick of such 'water service' as we are now experiencing and I hear of medical advice against its use. Teetotalism will fare ill unless a purer supply is obtained.*
> *Hull 8.12.1849*   *A Water Drinker.'*

A few weeks on, 7 March, 1850, another letter on the same subject appeared from someone who professed to have scientific knowledge. This writer believed there to be a connection between cholera and unwholesome water, citing the 20-30 per 10,000 cholera deaths in Thames-side areas such as Hammersmith and Kew, against the 231-268 per 10,000, lower down the river at Rotherhithe, where the water was polluted with the contents of sewers etc. As to Aikin and Taylor's analyses: 'The specimens submitted for analysis were taken at the close of last March, a period of the year most favourable for the absence of organic matter – judge then what it must be in the months of July and August, when . . . the Hull water is instinct with living organisms.' J. Murray, Ph.D., Portland Place.

A small item would have been noted by a careful reader of the *Herald* on 27 September, 1849, as the epidemic was coming to an end. 'Tendency of impure water to develope (*sic*) disease': In a small London square, half the inhabitants died after using pump water into which leaked foetid surface water containing a lot of organic matter.

James Smith's report THE SANATORY CONDITION OF HULL, dated 4 April, 1850, arrived in June of that year. It contained many sections on all aspects of public health. The water supply was considered in detail and faults which hitherto had come to general notice only through complaints, were set out in full. The engines at Stoneferry, intended to raise the water to 160ft., seldom did so, the actual working altitude being about 100-120ft.; during the day, giving rather strong pressure near the works, but not always sufficient at a distance. The full 160ft. was maintained during the night in case of fires. Water was supplied in periods of about three hours a day to each of the four districts into which the town was divided for that purpose. Tanks or cisterns were therefore used for storage. The cheapest cost about 12s.6d. to 15s. (62½p – 75p) but poor people made do with all kinds of container. 'As soon as the water is turned on to a district, every tap is opened and sometimes kept open until the supply is withdrawn.' Smith recommended a constant supply.

He then began the argument leading to his final conclusions. The Derringham water was conveyed by open channel for much of its flow, but although vulnerable to surface water and impurities, it did not receive sewage from nearby villages. The spring water's hardness was pretty much the same as the river's because both derive from the chalk, the contributory streams of the Hull arising in the higher Wolds beyond Beverley or Driffield. 'As the tide in the Hull flows nine miles above its junction with the Humber, the river is at the works filled at every tide with water which has flowed through the harbour where the bulk of the sewage from the town is discharged. However, the water is taken in only once every 24 hours at a state of the tide when there is least chance of impurities from nearer the river mouth entering the reservoir.' Marillier had told Smith that sometimes water was taken in for ten hours at a time, also that the water was never brackish in winter and only occasionally in summer. 'The other party', presumably Horner et al contended the water was brackish as far as Wawne Ferry at high spring tides and that deposits of mud and all kinds of floating matter were left on the banks to contaminate the water at all states of the tide. The emptying of Beverley's sewage into the river, the rank weeds which grew and decayed on the banks, the barges and other vessels churning up the mud and adding other pollutants to the water, were all pointed out to Mr. Smith, who said all that was obvious.

What did it amount to? How could it be removed?

Clark's process had been applied to the samples and as well as precipitating the chalk to soften the water, it also brought down a considerable amount of dark coloured matter', 'but how far the water is thus relieved of organic matter has not yet been ascertained.'

The soap tax was such a major factor, that hardness was considered first: 'Allowing that there are 16,000 families in Hull and that each uses only five gallons per day of water requiring the use of soap, softened water will give a saving of 365,000 lbs of soap to Hull at 6d (2½p) per pound. The cost of the burnt chalk required for the above quantity of water (i.e. to apply Clark's Process) would be about £7 per annum. Besides the saving in fuel, in washing labour, and in the wear and tear of clothes, there will be a great saving in the quantity of tea and affording a beverage much more agreeable in flavour. The general processes of cooking will be improved.'

Lyon Playfair's analysis had shown considerable organic matter, but no more so than elsewhere, so if the water were taken at the proper state of the tide, it would be 'wholesome and economical' for domestic purposes, 'and' continued Playfair, 'although it is not agreeable to know that the sewage water of Beverley and other places falls into the river, and that the tidal waters do deposit some slime on the banks, still it does not appear that the matter is appreciable in the large body of water in the River Hull.' This was Ayre's view.

Would the difference between the qualities of river and spring waters (continued Smith's report) warrant the expenditure of money necessary to bring water from the springs above Driffield to the pumping engine at Stoneferry, *'as it is evident that the Derringham Spring cannot nearly give an ample supply for Hull.'?* The cost of collection of water at Driffield and 2-foot iron piping to Stoneferry would not be less than £80,000, working out at about 5s. (25p) per year per house to the ratepayers, 'which, if the water really was very superior, would be no great sum to pay for it.' (Five shillings was half the recently-increased weekly wage of a street-cleaner.) It would be necessary and profitable to choose the softest source.

Smith presented all the local evidence he had taken in shorthand, to the General Board of Health, for its members to judge, but had not put it in the report as it was so contradictory.

The total number of houses supplied in February, 1849, was 17,410. Landlords generally paid the water rent for property under £10 p.a. rental, shipping was supplied by stand-pipes at the docks and local fishing vessels were charged 10s. (50p) per annum. Smith was not the first to note the favourable comments of seamen about the taste and keeping qualities of Hull water on long voyages. There was no *public* supply of water in the town, by taps or otherwise.

The general conclusions of Smith's Sanatory Report began, 'The rate of mortality is such that it demands intervention by the Board of Health.' Of the water supply: 'The present Waterworks will afford an ample supply of wholesome water for the inhabitants and shipping.' He put the cause of disease as the lack of sewerage, the open sewers, muck garths, etc.

So, even IF the 'poison' which caused the cholera was not in the water, the lack of a drainage system in which water would be more widely used, certainly was a major contributory factor.

The state of contemporary medical knowledge was shown in August, 1850, at a meeting of the Provincial Medical and Surgical Society with Dr. Horner in the chair as its new President. Among other items was a paper on the cholera compiled by Dr. Williams of Worcester, from evidence obtained by

Mr. Hunt of Bedford Square, London, and read by Mr. Sheppard. It may have been third hand, but it gave a more advanced picture than many of the ideas currently displayed in public debate in Hull.

'. . . It seemed to be almost universally believed that the disease depended upon a *bona fide* cholera *virus*, which, being admitted into the system, produced certain specific consequences. Another point almost universally believed was the facility of communication either from infected persons or things, by means of the clothing, atmosphere or evacuations.' The precise nature of the poison was not understood. 'Cesspools, burial grounds, defective ventilation, and want of cleanliness might influence the formation, operation or production of the poison either by having an alliance with it or predisposing the system for its reception.' Nothing had been proved regarding the condition of the atmosphere at the time of the malady's origin and some highly situated, well-drained and ventilated districts were attacked. Diluted chlorine invariably neutralised the poison. The cessation of an outbreak was as unaccountable as its origin.

Were any immune? – it seemed that butchers were, because they were well and strongly fed; cider drinkers and fruit eaters because of their good constitutions; and lead and arsenic workers because they were highly paid and able to live well. 'The most uniformly exempting causes were a vigorous state of mind and body, a vigorous diet, fresh air, exercise, temperance and cleanliness.' The vast majority of the victims were in a state of debilitation to start with 'As a means of preventing infection, carefulness in preventing communication with evacuations, and washing of hands and mouth after such as were necessary, and frequent changes of attendants, were recommended.'

'WAS IT THE WATER?' Nobody could give the right answer, because, as yet, nobody had asked the right questions.

1850 STONEFERRY IMPROVED

The tender of £6,019 from Witham's of Leeds to build an additional engine for Stoneferry was approved by Wicksteed and accepted by the Waterworks Committee in April, 1849. Although the cholera epidemic intervened, work was started, the new engine house finished by the end of the following March and the new Cornish engine of 30 tons beam was in course of erection.

By then, five years since the opening of the works, they were, in 1850, giving daily supplies equal to that which was calculated would be required 20 years from the opening. The *Eastern Counties Herald* indulged in a bit of 'we-told-you-so' in an article of 21 March, 1850. 'From the incorrect method of calculation in estimate, we stated at the time – before the Act was obtained – that the full power of the works would necessarily come into requisition much earlier than was calculated. No person, however, predicted that they would be so soon in full use.'

Two new reservoirs (6 acres, 1 rood of land, bought to receive the soil dug out from them, cost the Corporation £1,200) to act as filter beds had been excavated; they required new inlets and outlets, but apart from that and the new engine house and machinery no other alterations were needed, and it was confidently predicted that twice the amount of water could be supplied daily, at an outlay of not more than £10,000.

Alderman Thompson, Chairman of the Waterworks Committee since 1842, had believed in and worked for the establishment of the Stoneferry works and in Council had borne the brunt of the remarks of the detractors. Thompson believed, to the point of obstinacy, in the value of an *ample* water supply, but in this he was working for the good of the town within the limits of the knowledge of the time. His speeches and actions in Council and Committee give the impression of a man strong in mind and body; in fact he had started his working life as a poor country lad hoeing potatoes at sixpence a day. By the time he was made an Alderman in December, 1840, he was a merchant and shipowner, a growing force in the Council. The *Hull Free Press* mocked him as 'the presiding genius of the great salt lake at Stoneferry', but also praised his strength of character.

It was fitting that the new engine should be named after him.

It was started on Saturday, 13 July, 1850, in presence of the Alderman and several Committee members. A beam engine of 150 h.p., built by Mr. Wicksteed, the cylinder was of 75ins. diameter and the stroke 10ft. The plunger had a diameter of 30½ins. and the beam length 34ft. 8¾ins. 315¾ gallons were raised at each stroke, that is 2,841¾ gallons every minute or 2,046,000 gallons every 24 hours. '. . . When it started, it worked exceedingly easily and freely at the rate of 8 strokes per minute, pumping into the mains twice as much as do the other two put together, at a pressure of about 127ft. into the town.' Communication between this

Bust of Ald. Thomas Thompson in the Guildhall.
Photograph: Mr. A. McTurk.

To the Editor of the Eastern Counties Herald:

Dear Sir,

You represent, Sir, perhaps more nearly than you are aware of, what is likely to be the effect of a continued impurity in the water supplied to the town. Mrs. Nervous and I are, ordinarily, persons of exceedingly temperate habits and have hitherto been content with our modest glass a-piece after supper, enjoying it comfortably and without reproach. But, Sir, this state of things has been broken in upon. It is impossible to drink the water with which we have been supplied at any time within the last month or two; a dash of something stronger than itself is absolutely essential to swallowing it at all. The consequence of this is, that I am now in the condition of the late Mr. Pry, who was wont to say, pleasantly, "Mrs. P. and myself take a few mouthfuls of brandy after dinner on two occasions – when we have fish and when we have no fish."

. . . Now, after dinner, I feel dull and sleepy; Mrs. N. feels dull and sleepy; we doze off not unfrequently, wake up . . . not in the best of humours; and we have had words, Sir, – had words for almost the first time in our lives. Again, at night I don't feel satisfied or easy in drinking my formerly comfortable glass. Something says to me, "This is not the first today, Mr. N.; you are injuring your health; and you can't afford it, Sir." All this makes me irritable and unhappy – I who was wont to be, Mrs. N. says, fidgetty, but on the whole cheerful to a degree . . . And now, I write to you, Mr. Editor, entreating that you will use the influence of your journal to produce a wholesome supply of pure water for the good of the inhabitants at large, and that of

Your very Humble Servant,
Timothy Nervous.

Hull, 26th August 1850.

engine and the tower still had to be made, so water was, for the time being, pumped into an air vessel and thence directly into the mains. Once it was linked to the tower, promised the *Herald* article of 18 July, 'the town will then receive a constant supply of water.'

Several letters of complaint had reached the *Herald* during August and September, 1850, on the still unsatisfactory quality of the water. One, from 'Anti-Mud' suggested the addition of about ¼oz. of alum to each bucketful of water to clarify it. This idea was immediately seized upon by William Hendry, Surgeon, of 12, Dock Street who said that 'hardness' had been the hue and cry for some time and the alum would merely serve to increase that inconvenience, 'besides even threatening disease of the digestive organs'. 'My own impression is that a water requiring any chemical manipulation at all is unfit for use, and if *boiling and repose* will not effect the required changes, then the river water at its present point of supply is itself unfit for use.'

A letter from 'Timothy Nervous' was both an amusing insight into the state of things and also an indication that through the medium of the newspapers, the public hoped to influence the Town Council.

Dr. Horner was on his feet again in the Council meeting of 3 October, reminding his colleagues of his memorial of the previous year. At that time the Mayor (Ald. Lee Smith) had said the Hull water was no worse than that from the river Thames, an argument no longer tenable as the Thames water had been condemned. Liverpool and Manchester were at this time spending large sums on pure water supplies. Horner thought something should be done at once, as the water was unfit for domestic purposes 'and many persons got the-milkman to take them pure spring water in their carts. (Laughter)

Mr. Jackson: 'Do you mean in the milk?'

Horner, realising he had been beaten on the idea of a return to Springhead, now recommended that the water should be brought from a point four or five miles below Driffield, either by earthenware pipes or a culvert. He thought the land would cost nothing, (Mr. Bannister: Ask Mr. Haworth.) and moved that a committee be set up to enquire into the feasibility of such a plan. Dr. Ayre said the cholera had nothing to do with the water, which was purified by the very mud at the bottom of the river. There was bantering resistance to Horner's idea and although his motion was seconded by Jackson, it was negated by about three-quarters of the meeting, Ald. Abbey having seriously condemned the jocose nature of the debate upon a matter affecting the health of a large town.

A speaker at the Lit and Phil. meeting quipped with an epigram written to the Waterworks Committee:

> 'The Springhead water was decried
> Because the town's supply was poor;
> The river with its mud they bide
> Because its water's always *sewer*.'

The Public Health Act came into force for Hull in the summer of 1851 and in August the Town Council met as the Local Board of Health for the first time. Its early meetings were taken up with administration and the appointment of officials, including its surveyor. 55 candidates applied, including Cuthbert Brodrick, the architect, and the Board finally recommended Henry Newton, former Surveyor to the Myton Commissioners for the post, a recommendation not upheld by the General Board in London, because, they said, Newton was insufficiently qualified.

A CONSTANT SUPPLY

Discussing the report of the Inspector of Nuisances (another new post) at the end of December, 1851, the Local Board of Health's attention turned to the water question again. Dr. Ayre said there was 'a good supply' (i.e. in quantity), but Dr. Horner said it was not the number of gallons supplied that was important, but the number of hours during the day that it continued. The Mayor, Ald. Bannister, regretted Thompson's absence as 'he might have been enabled to inform the Board when the inhabitants of the town could obtain a constant supply.'

A real hint, then; it was going to happen and soon.

The long-awaited announcement came in a Public Notice of 8 January, 1852, informing the town that a trial was to be made of a constant supply and 'the water will be turned on to all parts of the town on Monday morning, the 26th inst. and left on Day and Night, with the exception of one hour, or more if necessary, each afternoon, (Sundays excepted) in order to allow time for repairing lead pipes . . .' Times of the shut-off in different districts were given and also the penalties for waste were set out.

That was almost fourteen years after the original Waterworks Committee was appointed.

NEXT TO GODLINESS

In September, 1846, an Act had became law, to enable authorities to provide baths and washhouses for the poor. The charges must be within the means of every rate-payer or burgess. By 10 August, 1847, a Baths and Washhouses Committee of the Town Council was in full operation, a far less sluggish group than the original Waterworks Committee, for on this date it recommended that a square plot of 1,127 sq. yds. in Trippett with houses and buildings on it, at that time let for £123.13s per annum, should be bought for £2,500 and upon it were to be built new baths and washhouses. This was accepted by the Town Council, a Mr. Bailey, selected as engineer, soon submitted plans and the meeting of 7 March, 1848, gave the go-ahead for work to begin.

An attempt to establish a private concern, the Hull Public Baths Co., in January, 1843, had come to nothing because of the building of the Hull and Selby Railway close to the Humber Bank where a site had been earmarked. A letter in the *Advertiser* in spring, 1840, complained that 'bathing-houses' on the riverside had been broken up and a new facility was needed. The Hull Public Baths Co. did finally come into being, although the public were slow in taking up the shares to raise the £3000 needed for the enterprise. Three years after the public meeting in the George, Bowlalley Lane, to re-start the project, the baths opened in May, 1843, on a site between Manor House Street and Cogan Street. (Manor House Street became the road leading up T-bridge going towards the river; Cogan Street was parallel to it to the west).

One major attraction was a spa on the premises or a well producing 'spa' water with a large proportion of marine salt, fullers' earth (making it soft) and chalybeate (iron). This water was a tonic and a powerful aperient.

After all the delays, 'The Public Baths are going swimmingly,' declared the *Herald* on 15 June, 1843. 'The warm baths are a perfect luxury . . . The spa water increases in transparency every day, and has lost the unpleasant smell which was observed in the first draughts.' All this was a tribute to Mr. Baker, the well-sinker, whose work had 'exceeded the highest expectation.'

Meanwhile, floating baths had been set up in Junction Dock by a Mr. Hudson and were, in the late summer of 1841, giving 'great satisfaction.' At the beginning of the following August they were moored near the piers. 'The water in these baths is salt and as clear as spring water and is considered to be exceedingly healthy.' It seems that these floating baths were part of Hull's waterfront scene for a year or two, but in late August, 1844, the vessel was sunk and became a partial wreck near the Corporation piers. This act of vandalism seems to have been the end of the enterprise as no other item about it appeared in the press.

The Hull Public Baths continued for those who could afford to patronise them, but the company's financial basis was fragile. The water, despite all its spa qualities, was sufficiently coloured to be off-putting, especially to ladies. Loans were raised to improve matters and enable the temperature of the large swimming bath to be increased from 70°F to 74°F.

By early summer, 1848, the company was not only still in operation, but the pump room had become a popular early morning rendezvous for middle-class men, many of whom made a habit of meeting there before breakfast. 'The spa water increases in demand, the more its medical virtue becomes known.'

Schoolboys and artisans were allowed in on Saturday afternoons at cheap rates. There had been a swimming master, a Mr. Bailey, but in the summer of 1848 'A Parent' wrote to the *Herald* wondering why he was not there and if he was too busy or too well paid at the New Holland Ferry where, presumably, he also had a job.

When, early in 1850, the company was suffering a severe shortage of funds, it offered its property to the Town Council for £1,500, which was less than the value of the materials it contained. By this time the Corporation already had baths at Stoneferry and the Trippett complex was well on the way to completion. The matter was discussed in Council rather more lengthily than it deserved, but various members, including the Mayor, Ald. T. W. Palmer, and the Sheriff, Ald. A. Bannister, declared they had an interest in the Company. The baths' elegance and style were praised; Dr. Horner said it would be a disgrace to the town if they were closed; and Cllr. Foster spoke of men who had travelled in Europe and America and declared that, except in Vienna, there were no baths to equal those at Hull. Cllr. Richardson was strongly against buying the Bath Company's property on the grounds that if there had been no councillor share-holders, the Town Council would have heard nothing of it, and to buy the Company would have been regarded as paying off the debt of any small joint stock company.

The Council did not buy; during 1852 some assets were realised and the building put up for sale. No more was heard of it via the newspapers.

Dr. Owen Daly gave a lecture 'On the Progress of Modern Baths and their Use' at the Lit. and Phil. meeting reported on 3 February, 1848. The chief point he made was for the necessity of more means for the public to wash frequently. Dr. Cooper called attention to the loss of ancient baths in Hull because of encroachment by the Iron Horse, but others had been opened on the Humber Bank. Mr. Lockwood, the architect, thought there should be baths and washhouses in different parts of the town, not just centrally, to which Daly pointed out that the establishments had to be big enough to make them pay. Mr. Lockwood further thought that baths should be made attractive, with coffee and newspapers while waiting, and Mr. Pearsall felt there was an especial need for baths in Hull because of the number of foreign visitors who were used to bathing.

The TRIPPETT BATHS AND WASHHOUSES were opened for inspection on Monday, 22 April, 1850, but 'the number of people that flocked to the place . . . was so great and the rudeness of some of them so conspicuous, that for the restoration of order which had been set at defiance and for the protection of the building, it became necessary at 2 o'clock to call in the police to clear the premises and to issue a fresh notice, which was immediately done . . . announcing the withdrawal of the privilege both of free use and of the inspection.' Small groups of properly conducted persons were then let in.

The buildings were complete except for the first class ladies' and first class gentlemen's private baths, which needed a few days longer. The total cost was over £12,000. The square tower, a feature of the east end of Queen's Dock and later of Queen's Gardens until the 1970s was both a furnace chimney and a ventilator for steam and foul air. Each private bathroom had a zinc bath and was supplied with coat pegs, a seat, a soap dish, etc. The water could be hot, cold or tepid; one penny for a cold bath, including a clean towel, and twopence for tepid or hot baths. (The Hull Public Baths had charged 1/6 (7½p) for a warm bath with a penny extra for a towel). There was also a plunge bath 'for ladies of the Hebrew nation'.

The laundry, as described in the *Eastern Counties Herald* of 25 April, 1850, 'contains 56 washing places, each of which has two tubs, one of which has a cover and a steam pipe for boiling clothes by means of hot water and steam; the other has two taps, one for hot, the other for cold water; each tub has a waste pipe and a tap so that there is no lifting of washing tubs; there is a shelf for wet clothes and a stick to use in the steam tub, plenty of room for a clothes basket and convenience for wringing. Besides all this, close to the washer's elbow is a plate of zinc in the form of a shutter with wheels and pulleys by which it slides up and down like a sash window; this shutter enters a closet or stove filled with hot air which dries the clothes as fast as they are washed' (actually it took about 30-40 minutes) 'without the possibility of scorching them. For use of all these things including hot water and cold, one penny per hour is charged for the first two hours and twopence per hour thereafter.'

Very heaven, one would think, for a woman who lived in one of the alleys in High Street, where only the previous October it had been reported that the water was 'on' merely two hours a day and the people paid sixpence a week for it. The *Herald* report was too early for many people to have heard of the new amenity and there were few takers, but more were expected. Never mind the scenes at the preview; the *Herald* told its readers that 'No brawling is allowed and therefore none takes place', and added to the list of delights afforded, the optional 'use of a patent mangle . . . and also the use of an ironing board 20ft. long and of a stove at which the irons are heated for nothing, so that the clothes may be brought dirty and taken back ready to wear.'

In the first week the use was as follows:

'2nd class baths, men, cold 34, warm 1,105
ladies, cold 16, warm 128
children 16
swimming bath 168.
Receipts from bathers, £12.8s.5d, from washers, 12s.7d. Surplus after wages etc. paid, £3.11s.10d.'

A long front-page article in the next week's *Herald* said, 'the wives of labouring men will regard the comfort of baths and the convenience of washhouses as luxuries which women in their condition have no right to expect or enjoy' – but when they find how easy washing day can be for 2d or 3d – then . . !

In the second week the surplus was up to £26.18s.7d (£26.93).

Bathing was, as expected, less popular in the winter than in summer, and the washhouses were used more in the winter.

With the scrupulous attention to statistics beloved of the Victorians the following report was presented to the Town Council, 10 May, 1852: 20 April, 1851 to 17 April 1852, inclusive:-

No. of bathers, 62,471, i.e. 54,755 men, 7,056 women, plus 660 children from the Workhouse.

Total received from bathing: £586.18s.3d (£586.91)

No. of washers, 6,536, who washed 23,388½ hours for which they paid £110.18s.2d.

There had been 19,284 less bathers than the year before, but a steady small increase in the number of washers.

The rumour that £2,000 was needed to put the place in order was denied, but it was stated that the Act of Parliament had fixed the charges so low that only a very large increase in the numbers using the amenities, would result in a profit. The rate, now 3d, would need to be doubled next year.

During the early 1850s, the various town authorities were concerned with regularising their affairs. The Baths and Washhouse rates were in the worst state, as the collectors, when they found they were short, employed an amount of chicanery to make up their losses. For example one of them, named Jefferson, admitted, 'upon my collection I had a small loss, but I trusted to the chapter of accidents to make it all right.' The Committee could not ascertain what was that 'chapter', nor how it was calculated to make it all right'. On another occasion a collector put ¼d on the rate himself, either to make up his deficit or put money in his pocket. This was a substantial increase on a 3d. rate. Mr. James Beeton, thus asked for the extra, said he would blow the system up, but the collector begged him not to do so. Beeton was a collector himself, but never discovered where the 'balances of other collectors went to, but he knew there was a particular year in which Jefferson had a balance in his hands of £162, and actually mentioned it, *but he was only a novice then.*' (Laughter). As the *Herald* commented 'The proceedings of the Local Board of Health and the Board of Guardians need watching . . . for. . . that which is renewed merriment to the members of the board is wormwood and death to the ratepayers.'

MUCK AND MONEY

A long leading article in the *Eastern Counties Herald* at the end of 1852 repeated the General Board of Health's warning about the spread of cholera across Europe, a menace that probably would strike Hull early on because of the 'intimate and incessant' trade links with Hamburg. A summary of the General Board's most constant and most repeated recommendations followed. The value of a constant water supply was implicit: 'The General Board's measures of internal and external cleansing are all practicable and involve little expense. Surface washing by hose or jets could be easily carried out in Hull where such a head of water can be obtained. Privies and cesspools can be emptied by force pumps and suction pipes more economically than by manual labour and with much less offensiveness to the neighbourhood, especially if deodorisers are freely used.'

'When Mr. Edwin Chadwick and Mr. Smith of Deanston visited Hull in 1843 they contemplated sanitary reforms which seemed at that time of unattainable perfection and efficacy. They looked forward to a time when the drains would be flushed once a day by an irresistible head of water which should remove the excreta of towns, and every animal and vegetable substance in the drains, before decomposition should have time to take place. But experience has shown that flooding the sewers is not the best mode of cleansing them, and experiments, under the direction of Mr. Chadwick as to the best shape, and form, and material of drains, have shown that refuse can be carried from our dwellings by a silent and continuous course of removal. The new method of drainage is effected by a constant supply of water in connection with the water closet system and small drainpipes of glazed earthenware or stoneware of tubular shape.'

This system would get rid of all privies and cesspools. Every house, however small, must have its water closet and 'must be compelled to have a supply of water. Half measures will not do.'

This is a tremendous change in attitude from that of the 1838 Waterworks Committee, who believed that the whole town could be supplied with enough water for an outlay of about a thousand pounds. The use of water as a scouring, cleansing agent required an ample supply that was both constant and at a good pressure. Quantity had been ensured by Ald. Thompson and his Committee cutting through the objections and developing the Stoneferry scheme, but their decision to try a constant supply was largely brought about by public opinion and even by the anti-Stoneferry group, especially Dr. Horner. By now filth was totally equated with the origin of disease and the question of drainage, rather than water supply, was the major public health concern of the early 1850s in Hull.

James Smith of Deanston was particularly keen on the use of sewage as an agricultural fertiliser. One of the questions of the 1843 survey was, 'What places are used for the deposit of the refuse of the town and to what extent is it sold for productive use as manure?' The answers took Smith to the muck garths and muck gatherers, private enterprises that brought nothing into the town's coffers.

During his visit, Smith had seen the flushing of the drains in the old town. The Commissioners had first seen the floodgate in Lowgate tied up and then went to the mouth of the main drain in Nelson Street where it emptied into the Humber. 'A flood of water from the Old Dock rushed along the whole course of the drain, and came tumbling out at the mouth in black and filthy volumes, sufficiently indicative of the accumulated impurities which it held in suspension . . . We could not help thinking,' continued the *Herald*, 'that Mr. Smith regarded the inky stream with an anxious, if not envious eye, as it flowed into the Humber, as if he would fain have conveyed the fertilising particles of animal and vegetable matter into some neighbouring farmer's field instead of thus suffering it to run to waste.' The best system of drainage the Commissioners were then able to suggest was a gigantic flushing system 'in which every description of refuse, night soil, etc., will be swept away through our drains by a flood of pure water every morning,' and this would be carried in close drains to the countryside to act as fertiliser.

Edinburgh had adopted a similar scheme with such success that the town could afford to clean every street, court and alley every day, because it sold about £10,000 worth of manure per annum. In nearby Dalkeith, with a population of only 5,200, the sale of manure allowed for cleaning every street, court and alley (and twice on Saturdays) with a surplus of £100 per annum. The second report of the Health of Towns Commission had given these facts and also commented on the peculiar situation in Hull where 'the inhabitants have there found out that they can profitably collect, with great regularity, the refuse from houses, even in the courts and alleys which are inaccessible to carts. This is carted away without any aid on the part of the local authority'. And then the sting in the tail: 'At Hull, the regular removal of refuse is an accident, and as far as the authorities are concerned, the poor are as much neglected as elsewhere.' The report proposed to give local authorities in England, sole property in the removal of night soil.

Technical advances in the production of earthenware pipes of larger diameters had been made in the years between the 1845 Health of Towns Report and the 1852 *Herald* article, but although possibilities of a different system were in view, the idea of using sewage as a fertiliser persisted.

In the years that followed the riches to be derived from sewage fertiliser were lost sight of, in the battles that developed about the ways in which the drainage of Hull could be accomplished.

EAST VERSUS WEST

The quarterly return of the Registrar General showed that in the latter part of 1850, Hull was the only town in which any appearance of epidemic cholera was observed. During the last quarter of that year, 74 people died of the disease, with deaths in nearly every district. The reduction in cases in Hull and other towns was ascribed to the progress in sanitary measures after the 1849 epidemic. Wide powers had been given to local authorities by the provisions of the 1848 Public Health Act, one of which was that maps of sewerage were to be made and to be accessible to ratepayers. 'No new house can hereafter be built without drains, privies, etc.'

William Clark, C.E., the newly-appointed Surveyor to the Local Board of Health, who had replaced Henry Newton because the General Board in

London had found Newton insufficiently qualified, gave two lectures on The Drainage and Sewerage of Large Towns to the Lit. and Phil. early in his career as Surveyor. He stressed the superiority of glazed pipes over flat-bottomed brick sewers because of the latter's greater cost in labour and flushing and also because filth tended to accumulate in them. He said that engineers had been too concerned with main drains, leaving small house drains for the builder to put in just as he liked, and very often they fell into the main drain against the proper flow. Instances of this had been noted by the Commissioners in 1843. Again the idea of sewage as fertiliser was voiced, Clark estimating that from a town, population 99,000, a profit of £12,000 a year could be made.

The Local Board received a set of instructions from the General Board a few months later, including the use of tubular house drains, without the use of brick or stone, as Clark had described in his lecture.

The Ordnance Survey of the early 1850s gave Hull the opportunity to have a subterranean survey in which detailed measurements of the levels were obtained, just when they were needed.

Clark drew up a plan for draining the district east of the River Hull. Apart from the Groves and a cluster round Drypool and the Citadel, this was flat, agricultural land, virtually unoccupied by houses.

It had a few natural streams and some ditches that had been dug as much to provide boundaries as for drainage. Clark believed that pumps should be used to ensure a constant flow and this was endorsed by his successor, Newman, when Clark left to take up a post in India. The matter went as far as an Act to carry out the drainage of the East District at a cost of £12,000 and work was started in 1854. In 1856, however, at the Local Board of Health, Cllr. Galloway put the motion:

'That there be an alteration in the plan for the main sewer and outfall for the East District, so as to make the drain self-acting, and to dispense with the engines and pumps; and to rescind any resolution by the Board heretofore passed which may be contrary to this resolution.'

A plan was already on the table for the West District, the idea being to see how the East District scheme worked before proceeding in West Hull. There were four hours of debate and finally Galloway's plan was accepted. Newman, the Surveyor, did not agree with it. Dr. Cooper (by now he was Sir Henry Cooper) said that the great object to be attained was the health of the town. Drainage was the means. For drainage to be effective, it must be constant, which meant sufficient fall, and this had to be maintained by pumping. 'As to Mr. Galloway's plan of letting the sewage out only with the tide, it would then – loaded with dead animals and other impurities – float about and settle on the banks of the Humber, there putrefying and becoming a source of disease.' Mr. Todd quoted the case of Croydon, where the General Board had sanctioned a system in which the sewage liquid ran into the local river, causing a great number of cases of fever and diarrhoea and many deaths; so much for the infallibility of the General Board!

Alderman Moss was the great champion of the West Drainage plan and the passage of Cllr. Galloway's resolution on 1 February, 1856, would mean further waiting for the West District Drainage to be carried out. Now, with between £7,000 and £8,000 already spent in the East District, there was a complete change of plan, necessitating the removal of the pumps. Moss felt they should not be experimenting, but should get a person of some eminence to advise them and therefore, not as a member of the Local Board of Health, but as a 'responsible citizen' wrote to the General Board of Health in London, appraising them of the situation.

Their reply was the official 'Any alterations the Local Board wished to make must be notified to the General Board.'

In a Local Board meeting in October, 1857, Moss was charged with remarks he had made at a lecture to the National Association for the Promotion of Social Science in Birmingham. He replied to the charge by saying that he was illustrating the delay that took place in carrying into effect sanitary measures, by reference to the cholera having carried off 2,000 of the inhabitants of Hull, and stating that the system of drainage had not been altered 'since we, as a Board of Health, became aware of its connexion with the prevalence of disease in 1849.' Boards should be left to their duties, he continued, but if they would not, 'there should be a public minister to see that they did their duties.'

At the end of 1857 the outcome of the East District experiment, with the pumps removed, was still awaited and the West District was still not drained. Unfortunately Ald. Moss was not liked by a section of the Board. Percival Lambert said in the meeting of 22 December, 1857, that the Board should retain its independence against the threat of Mr. Moss and his attempt to establish a dictatorship in the borough.

Without the advice of a truly competent and independent expert on drainage the matter dragged on, with acrimony in the meetings and little done on the ground. The East District experiment would take a further two years, it was said, and at the end of 1857 Newman had resigned. Marillier was appointed Surveyor and also retained his position as engineer at the waterworks.

By then the Water Question was again very much to the fore.

BACK TO SPRINGHEAD?

Although the water question did not receive much press coverage after the installation of the Thompson engine and the start of a constant supply in 1852, there were occasional letters of complaint about the water. For example, a very civilly-worded letter from 'A Ratepayer' stated that 'in its unfiltered state (and that, of course, in which it is used by a great and valued portion of the community, viz. the working classes), it is totally unfit for use, and the sight of it on the table in a transparent vessel is disgusting.' 'Unfiltered' meant the water as received; it had passed through the Stoneferry filtration process, but the poor could not afford extra water filters of their own.

Then in July, 1857, the Waterworks Committee resolved to consider a petition from local brewers praying that water be taken from higher up the river. By this time Ald. Mayfield was chairman of the committee and he and Marillier, the engineer, set about investigating further possibilities of the River Hull. In October, Marillier submitted a report. He had taken levels from Stoneferry for 4¾ miles upstream as far as Wawne Ferry. The tide rarely went so far up and there was a bar at the Ferry which would ensure good water above it, he said. The fall to the works was only about 4ft. or one foot per mile; in dry times, less. At present they were able to supply 3½ million gallons a day, but Marillier thought that 6 million gallons should be provided. A pipe or culvert of 33 inches diameter would be needed, Marillier favouring a cast iron pipe, which alone would cost about £27,000, exclusive of expenses for law and land. Should it be decided, however, to go even higher up the river, above Beverley Beck to Hull Bridge, the shortest main to the works would be 7 miles and it would be necessary to pump the water that distance. The cost of engines, buildings and a 22-inch main would work out at about £6,000 per mile, again exclusive of law or land, and there would be considerable additional annual expenditure due to the pumping.

Ald. Mayfield annexed a letter containing his own views on the subject to Marillier's report, for presentation to the Waterworks Committee. Mayfield observed that much about the Stoneferry works seemed to have been faulty. For example, the position of the entrance basin at the bend of the river

allowed considerable surface impurity to enter and go into the reservoirs because it was stirred up when the gates were opened to admit water to the reservoir; and also the current at the river bend drew rubbish into the entrance basin. Further, since the works were opened, 'several large manufactories, employing hundreds of hands, have been erected on the banks of the river . . . and most offensive matter is daily poured into

Example of a water filter at Yorkshire Water's Museum, Springhead.

Photograph: Mr. A. McTurk. By kind permission of the Senior Keeper, Mr. D. W. Atkinson

it in large quantities and carried up by the tide above the waterworks.' At neap tides it no doubt became mingled with the fresh coming down river and was admitted to the reservoirs; also at high tides, especially in the autumn, salt was carried for five miles above Stoneferry and so the water was sometimes salt.

His own observations corroborated by Marillier, Mayfield called for an inquiry into the possibility of a uniformly pure supply. He did not think it possible to make a precise estimate of the effect of a water supply upon people's health, but he was aware of the medical knowledge of the time and said, 'It has been proved that whereas pure water seems not capable of receiving or generating the infective principles of cholera, on the other hand impure water appears to be one of the readiest means of conveying it into the system.' Mayfield seemed at that time to have been open-minded and forward-looking – a far cry from the remark of Mr. Barrick, Workhouse Governor, back in October, 1850, 'The Board know my opinion very well I care very little about epidemics, for to say it at once, I am a fatalist.' Or the back-pedalling attitude shown in Beverley, where in May, 1852, it was considered premature to appoint a treasurer to the recently-constituted Board of Health as they were 'merely feeling their way to ascertain the least possible extent to which they would be compelled to carry out the provisions of the Public Health Act, which had, unfortunately, been brought into operation in Beverley.'

With such a neighbour up-river, what did the Stoneferry works take in?

THE STONEFERRY MIXTURE

Water supplied from the Stoneferry works soon became known as the Stoneferry Mixture, or *Potage a la Mayfield*, the components of which were the subjects of letters to the press and comments in Council and elsewhere. Cllr. Denison reported to the Town Council in December, 1861, that one day the water had 'several tons of whitening in it; on another, the mud of the Humber,' followed by Cllr. Dowsing's revelation that 'he lately took an eel out of his water tap, the length of his arm and nearly as thick.' Complaints about the water's saltiness were common and had been so since 1845, the opening of the Stoneferry works.

A letter received by Ald. Mayfield sums up the sheer frustration felt by many householders:

Postmark date, 19 December, 1857.

Sir,
You must excuse me for writing, but I have been informed that you are on the Committee to look after the water, and as I only get

*tea at home sometimes, when I sat down tonight, I wished both
you and all the Comite drowned in it; only taste yourself and
then I think you will agree with me. Mister Todd said we should
all have better water. He may have at barton, and you may drink
hessle water, so that hull water my be good for ought you know.
Only drink a glass tonight, and then you will find what the poor
as to drink.*

    From a poor man who has had his tea spoild tonight.
*P.S. – If you are not in fault, they must be all drunk at the
Waterworks.-.'*

The factories lining the river Hull were, in the 1850s, varied enough either
to allow solid or fibrous matter to enter the water, or to contaminate the
water chemically. Some of the pollutants, although inconvenient and
unpleasant, were not particularly harmful or likely to cause infectious
disease. Flax and cotton mills; gas, paint, soap and cement works; tar and
turpentine distilleries; oil and flour mills and associated warehousing; bone
crushing and artificial manure works; foundries and engineering shops were
all listed in contemporary directories and there were also the tanneries at
Beverley which troubled the anti-Stoneferry group almost as much as the
Hull factories did. There were also worries about the drainage from the
General Cemetery, which ultimately found its way into the river.

More sinister than anything from the manufacturing processes was the
amount of sewage that went into the river, not only as a matter of course
from the old town drains and from Beverley and other places upstream, but
also from whatever conveniences were used by the increasing number of
workers in the riverside factories. And from the rats.

On 17 July, 1858, the *Hull Free Press* became quite poetical about the
river:

    'The meeting of the waters.

    There is not in the wide world a river so sweet
    As the Hull when the tide and its backwaters meet,
    When the scent-laden treasures from Beverley run black
    And commix with the fumes from the slime on its bank.

    Yet it is not the bone-boiling bouquet you smell
    Nor the blue-billy streams from the gas works that well,
    'Tis not patent manure-works that fragrance distil,
    O no, it is something more odorous still.

    'Tis the rich cordial compound that gushingly comes
    From the labours of those who would sweeten our homes,
    And we sensibly feel how our case we improve
    By combining for all what we strive to remove.

Sweet vale of the Hull! and thy luscious old tide,
Where the mud-banks, perennial, embellish thy side,
And ne'er while thy redolent stream ebbs and flows
Shall the smell of thy garbage depart from my nose.'

C. S. Eccles in his little memoir on the history of the Springhead works, tells how the better-off fared:

'At that time (1858) I resided in Minerva-terrace, Spring Bank, and a man from Hessle with a large water-cart came round regularly, and I bought of him at a penny per bucket all the water I required for drinking purposes. The deputy chairman of my Election Committee had relatives living at Barrow-on-Humber, and he had three small barrels – one on tap with water from there, one in transit, and one at Barrow. He paid the carriage of his supplies from Lincolnshire in preference to using the contaminated Stoneferry water.'

1857-8: 'TO BE FULLY AND FAIRLY TESTED'

On Boxing Day, 1857, the *Advertiser* printed a long letter from Thomas Stather, engineer, who, having seen that the Town Council had brought up the subject of water yet again, offered a few facts to the argument. He had been a Hull resident for nearly 30 years, during which time he had had a good deal to do with boring into the rock to provide water for steam engines. Stather had no hesitation in declaring that there was plenty of water for all the bores he had made or come across in his work, and he refuted the idea, voiced in Council, that if two bores were made close together, one would exhaust the other. He cited the case of Mr. Petchell's mill in High Street, now occupied by Mr. Darling. The bore there had been yielding night and day for years, producing more than 140 gallons per minute. Only about 20 yards away, a new 7-inch bore was put down to service an engine for Mr. Hodge and it had been giving 280 gallons per minute for the past 3 or 4 months. In Green Lane a mill had two bores only a few feet apart and Earle's Cement works had three bores close together which had been working for 17 to 18 years producing 300 gallons a minute. He acknowledged that the quality of the water was unsuitable for domestic purposes, being often quite 'brack' and not fit to drink, but the water was better to the west of Hull than to the east and if a pipe were put into the rock, good water could be obtained in west Hull. For example, water from just beyond the cemetery was tested at a lecture by Mr. Sollitt, Head Master of the Grammar School, and found to be of excellent quality.

Mr. Stather's letter went on, 'I do believe that almost any quantity could be got from the Derringham Springs and of first rate quality at less expense than any other means within our reach.' If the Spring Ditch were deepened to about 12ft. and 25 four-inch bores made in it between Botanic and Springhead, they would utter not less than five million gallons of water in 24 hours and he conjured up the picture of 25 fountains playing along the centre of the Spring Ditch from these bores. Stather suggested a proper culvert or pipe from Springhead to Botanic and possibly a water-wheel at the old works to give a head of water for distribution. Even if the springs' output was reduced at any time, there was still the Stoneferry works to supply enough for the town.

This was one of several overtures from local practical men who had had dealings with minor water supplies by means of bores and wells. Sometimes a letter to the press was sufficient to trigger at least a comment during the following Waterworks Committee meetings but not in this case. The Committee in mid-January, 1858, were preoccupied with a seeming error of judgement on Marillier's part some time before; he had let water into the reservoirs when it would have been better not to do so and there were complaints. Members of the Committee were not experts. On this occasion Cllr. Galloway said he understood there was a test of a water's quality and 'If there had been any such thing applied in this case, there would not have been spoiled some £500 worth of tea. (Laughter; cries of 'Cream!')'

It was the Town Council, not the Waterworks Committee, that received the next request from the public in the form of a 900-signature memorial, complaining of the unwholesome and offensive water from Stoneferry and requesting that the capability of the Derringham Springs be tested fully and fairly, this to be done immediately and without sparing effort or means, to obtain a supply from some source other than the river at Stoneferry.

This was acted upon and soon a major test of the Derringham Springs was under way. Trial bores were made and pumping started. Peculiarities were noted: that there was a copious supply from 30ft. down, but it was not so plentiful at 60ft.; also the quality from the bores differed greatly from the naturally issuing spring water. At least, said the *Advertiser* on 13 February, 1858, for 'dietetic purposes' the springs could supply enough and perhaps a double row of pipes could provide a dual supply, using both spring and river water separately.

The experiment was the talk of the town and according to the *Advertiser* the war waxed fierce between the two parties, pro-spring and pro-river. A third party sprang up, advocating the dual supply to use both sources. Up to 20 February, 1858, the talk was really thin air, as all that had been done were trial bores and the construction of a gantry for the machinery. Two engines of six and nine horse-power were used to pump from the four principal springs into which pipes had been driven down as far as the chalk. One rotary and three reciprocating pumps were employed. The water thus pumped up was directed by sluices into the Spring Ditch, thence to the old Botanic reservoir and then through the town sewers. Pumping went on well into March, but 'pump as they will, not more than ¾ million gallons can be got within the 24 hours, whilst our daily consumption is more than 3 million gallons.' Those for the springs said there was plenty of water to be got; the experiment should be fully and fairly tried. Opponents said that even if there was enough water there, it would cost more than the town would be prepared to pay. Better far go higher up the river at less cost.

The engineer chosen to carry out this experiment was, like Wicksteed, a professional engineer from London. He was James Simpson of Westminster, and, as with Wicksteed, great things were expected of him.

An influential paper on 'The Supply of Water' was read to members of the Royal Institution by James Oldham, C.E., on 10 March, 1858. Oldham spoke of Artesian wells, which had been introduced into this country about 1790, and he gave instances of Artesian wells in the Hull district, some made under his direction: at the Zoological Gardens, less than 50ft depth; near North Bridge, 65ft.; a little to the west of the Humber Dock basin, 110ft.; Hodge's mill, Holderness Road, (site of the present Morrill Street Clinic) 84ft.; and at Sunk Island, 110ft. to the rock. Oldham thought the Derringham Springs should never have been abandoned, but should have been fully tested before Stoneferry was built. He believed the springs would yield far more than the town would ever require, but pumping from the basin of the springs would never give the necessary test. Further, since there were works at Stoneferry, if an Artesian well would answer, why not bore down to the rock there? Marillier's suggestion of water from above Wawne, or even above Hull Bridge, would not provide a supply free of sewage. For that, it would be necessary to go further, to the West Beck, a feeder stream discharging into the Driffield Canal about a mile above Struncheon Lock and take water from Corps Landing, about two miles from Cranswick Railway Station. Water here was as good as the river could provide, as it had flowed over gravel shoals.

Oldham also proposed that the inadequately low outfalls of the Barmston, Skidby and Cottingham Drains should be obviated by channelling all of them to a single outfall on the Humber west of Hull, and the Holderness Drain, then coming into the River Hull at North Bridge, should be diverted to a Humber outfall near Marfleet. He again proposed, as he had done in 1836, a lock on the River Hull about opposite Humber Street, to convert the river into a kind of dock which could be maintained at a constant level by careful management of the lock gate. It would be a good idea, anyway, he said, to have a lock gate on the river between the outfall of the Skidby drain (opposite the junction of Cumberland and Church Streets) and the Stoneferry waterworks, to shut out the tide and improve the quality of the Stoneferry water. Oldham envisaged that such plans could be financed jointly by the waterworks and the Driffield Navigation.

One wonders if this *tour de force* was self-advertisement, saying, in effect, that there was at least one engineer as capable and farsighted in Hull as any in London.

Taking part in the discussion after Oldham's lecture was Dr. Horner, by then a reluctant advocate of a source much higher up the river, and since he had examined the river with Oldham, he agreed that the West Beck was the best source. 'But he begged to assure the audience that chemical analysis was good for nothing in testing properties of the water in so far as these were concerned with the health of people. There had been several cases where chemical analysis pronounced a water to be good, but a microscope revealed the presence of a very dangerous fungus, he said.

Simpson's Springhead experiment continued. As the *Advertiser* put it in 'Local Gossip', 20 March, 1858, 'Water is the subject of fluent talk yet, and the public interest is thoroughly fixed on the matter.' It was going to be a belt-and-braces trial; should Simpson report against the Springs, the Council would call in local engineers to give *their* verdict. It was said that the springs as such were pumped dry every day without yielding a million gallons; the bores, meanwhile, produced water apparently unfit to drink, but Simpson was going to have it tested and if it was good enough he would see how much could be got from these bores and similar ones.

Ald. Thompson was Mayor at the time, although now the Chairmanship of the Waterworks Committee was in the person of Ald. Mayfield. Rumours that Thompson had tried to impede the experiment were current in the town, but 'Local Gossip' assured readers that 'no man in Hull is more anxious than the Mayor to have the sources of supply in the Derringham Springs direction fully tested; because he feels convinced that it will settle for ever the question as to where the supply of water shall come from, and so settle much unpleasant feeling in the town.'

By late March tongues were still wagging but heads were also shaking. There were insinuations that the trial was not being carried out as fully and as fairly as promised. The Myton Reform Association sent a memo. to the Town Council which alleged (that is not too strong a word) that the Springhead test was not utilising all the possible means for a full and fair trial. The Association urged the Council 'to carry out without loss of time such measures as will place the extent of the productiveness of the springs beyond doubt or conjecture.'

The Waterworks Committee was in a difficult position, because to test exhaustively could be expensive; it could mean exploration outside the area then being tested, even to go to likely places between Hessle and Market Weighton. There was, of course, a limit to which they could count on the support of the Council and the electors, for if the trials brought a negative result, the Committee would be accused of spending money on a wild goose chase.

Simpson, according to Cllr. Middleton, speaking at the Market Place Ward meeting at the beginning of April, had an almost world-wide reputation to sustain. Simpson was at the time trying deeper bores and analysing the water thus obtained. It was revealed at the same meeting that the Stoneferry water was sometimes muddy because the filters got choked up and unfiltered water was distributed to the town while the filters were being cleaned.

Simpson was much of his time in London, having left Mr. Husband as overseer of the works. Marillier was the liaison between the work in hand and the Council, a very uneasy position. Judging by the correspondence between Marillier and Simpson published in the papers, it seemed that Marillier wanted to put into practice some of the ideas current in the town, many of which were his own. Simpson seemed to be working by the book to some extent. Of course, Marillier was on hand to see what was happening (and hear what was said) day by day. Not only was Mr. Witt, a London chemist, in the service of Mr. Simpson, analysing the water, but also, according to Marillier, some of the local chemists, including Pearsall and Sollitt, had done so. The locals pronounced the bore water as of 'unexceptional quality'. As a professional engineer Simpson had matters other than the present test to occupy him and Marillier's correspondence was usually in the form of a goad to urge him to try something else at Springhead. Simpson agreed it would be advisable to open the spring holes down to the chalk, but told Marillier not to start any big works until he had got the written report from Mr. Witt (which would be some time) and had opportunity to consider the matter.

There was a conflict between the engineer Simpson, who presumable knew what he was doing at a technical level, and the practical advice, sometimes sanctioned by Simpson, sometimes not, with which Marillier was urging both the Committee and the engineer to get on with things. There is a sense of frustration in Marillier's letters to Simpson and his reports to the Committee. One resolution in Council to act upon Marillier's report ended, '. . . provided Mr. Simpson do not object thereto,' which possibly showed that the Councillors felt that Marillier had a better grasp of the situation than Simpson had.

1858 WILLIAM WARDEN WRITES.

There then arrived one of the most important communications the Town Council were to receive concerning the water supply. A letter, dated 24 March, 1858, came from William Warden, plumber, of Hessle, to Ald. Mayfield as Chairman of the Waterworks Committee:

> *Sir,*
> *There appearing to be many conflicting opinions as to whether there is a sufficient supply of pure water to be obtained at Springhead, I beg to make the following proposition, viz, that I will engage to procure five million gallons of pure water daily, on*

condition that I shall receive £500 if I fulfil my engagement, or nothing if I fail. I am prepared to enter into an agreement to perform the contract. I may observe that the materials to be used would be such as would be required for the permanent working of the springs when in operation.

I am, Sir, yours very truly,
William Warden.

It was Cllr. Jackson who coined the phrase 'no cure, no pay' to summarise Warden's offer, after complaining that the Springhead experiment under Simpson's direction had been sluggishly carried out and that the last six weeks had been wasted. Mayfield gave some slight apology for Simpson by saying the work was by no means routine and there had been natural difficulties which could not be foreseen. Mayfield thought they should wait until Mr. Witt's analysis was received via Simpson; he made some criticism of Marillier because the Council had appointed Simpson, so Marillier should have consulted him and acted under his instructions. However, Mayfield still thought that recourse should be made to local practical men if Witt's analysis was unfavourable. 'Nothing should be left undone in promoting the town's interest. (hear, hear)'

Alderman Thompson made a long speech justifying his actions with regard to Stoneferry. He was proud of the works there. 'They were good ones and worth all the money they cost, if only for the extinguishing of fires.' (£60,000 plus!) As to Simpson, Thompson said they had employed a man who would do his duty – let them trust him. And as to Warden's offer, let them not imagine he would get the water for £500; that was a fee in case he did and the Council would have to bear the cost of the experiment.

When Witt's analysis came, it showed the Springhead water to be pure enough, but West Beck purer still. The choice depended on cost . . . or faith.

Pumping went on through April, producing only ¾ million gallons per day. Two propositions were put to

Portrait of William Warden at Yorkshire Water's Museum, Springhead.

Photograph: Mr. A. McTurk. By kind permission of the Senior Keeper, Mr. D. W. Atkinson

Simpson from the Waterworks Committee meeting of 22 April 1858, one to make a 12-inch bore, the other to sink an ordinary well-shaft. His reactions were awaited.

'There does not seem to be any probability of the gossip as to the water supply exhausting itself, although the Derringham Springs may . . . There is one party that sticks to the springs as a source of our water supply with a tenacity which is really wonderful, and when it turns out that the water will not come from the source in sufficient quantity for our requirements, they lay all the blame on Mr. Simpson . . . On the other hand it is contended that the experiments which have been made at Springhead demonstrate the fact that the Springs will not supply the town . . . Mr. Simpson reports that he thinks by making numerous bores, he could get ten million gallons per day at an expense (without giving details) of from £70,000 to £80,000. It is said that this expense may be much larger . . . when the details are given; that Mr. Simpson tells us that upon careful estimate ten million gallons per day can be brought from Hull Bridge for £99,000, and that it will be much wiser to go to a source, the ability of which to supply the town with good water there can be no doubt, than to waste money over what may be fruitless experiments.'

A letter from Simpson in the same issue of the *Advertiser* (12 June, 1858) set out his belief in a supply from boreholes, but there could be problems in obtaining lands on which to sink the wells and also parliamentary or legal difficulties. He did not think the present knowledge of the springs was sufficient to rely on them for the town's needs.

Both Simpson and Baker, the well-borer, were at the 19 May meeting of the Waterworks Committee. More surface area was required and a resolution was put to negotiate with Mr. Walker and other owners of property adjoining the springs for the use of their land.

At the next meeting, a letter from another local man, John Speck, well-borer of Hessle, was read. He engaged to get between 3 and 5 million gallons a day from the Derringham Springs by putting down thirty 6-inch boreholes, each to yield 10,000 gallons per hour, 'for the sum of £250, and if I do no get that quantity, I will only £150 (*sic*); but I can get any quantity for when I bored the three holes it let me now there is a very great supply of water . . . I have been a well-borer for 25 years in the neighbourhood and I now all the fishers in the rocks in the district. The bore I made at the Hessle Station is a 4-inch bore and I know it will throw 15,000 gallons per hour, and all the thirty 6-inch bores at the Derringham Springs will be overflowing ones if I bore them . . .'

At this meeting, Simpson's report was considered. He had had a good deal of experience in chalk districts and believed that wells in those areas were a better answer to the problem than rivers 'which are becoming more polluted by drainage.' For Springhead, he suggested a shaft of iron cylinders of 9ft. 6ins external diameter to a depth of 40ft., then sink 30ft. further and from this depth of 60-70ft. to tunnel sideways in various directions towards the springs making drifts or adits of 5ft 6ins by 3ft 6ins. He thought that drilling any deeper would reach objectionable water as they had in fact encountered an oxide or carbonate of iron that gave a mineral taste to the water in a borehole 80ft. deep.

It was moved by Mayfield and seconded by Samuelson, that the Springhead experiments be immediately discontinued. This was carried.

The cost of the experiments was £635.18s.10d (£635.91) so far, of which £220.3s.2d (£220.16) was unpaid. Simpson sent a letter about Speck's offer, saying it was 'opposed to geological conditions and reasoning upon the subject.' In this letter also, was a sentence underlining Hull's problems and problems elsewhere, as many towns had established their waterworks earlier in the century and were finding them inadequate in quantity or quality or both, for 'of late years the tendency of the publications issued by the General Board of Health has been to direct attention of the inhabitants of towns to the advantages of supplies of water delivered by means of waterworks, not only for domestic use, but for sanitary and manufacturing purposes, and the requirements are going on in a greater ratio than the increase of population from the fact, that water is now used for baths and other services which the inhabitants could not avail themselves of when the supplies were not so abundant, convenient or accessible.'

In the Town Council meeting a few days later, the above report was acknowledged in the Waterworks Committee minutes, but then Samuelson said another report had been received from Simpson that day (30 June) which might alter some people's opinions. This was virtually Simpson's swan song. He put forward the usual alternatives with little modification; a shaft to be sunk immediately, at the site of the present springs and tested for a year; if inadequate, go to the river above Hull Bridge, but not at once because of the prejudice against the river water; if Springhead were inadequate, springs nearer to Anlaby, known to be of better quality, might serve, but would not yield as much as Springhead.

It was really an impasse; everything suggested would take much more time and money.

However, the Council discussion veered away from Simpson's report when Jackson asked why the experiment had been stopped.

Mayfield: 'It was discontinued at Simpson's request, as his purpose had been answered and there was no need to continue further.' This does not seem to be totally true; there were signs that the Council was becoming irritated by Simpson's absences and the whole business seemed to be getting nowhere. Jackson thought the experiment should continue. He produced a bottle of Stoneferry water which, he said, was full of animalculae and was utterly unfit for household use. He thought it was high time something was done, when water like this was supplied to the town. Cllr. Richardson, who, some weeks before had said the Stoneferry water was good, ridiculed Jackson for handing round the sample: 'These animalculae happened to be not water animals at all, but intestinal worms which were to be found in beetles, and which, when they got the master of the beetles, would eat them up. The animalculae, therefore, were not to be treated as being bred in the water.' Richardson was a dentist, well known for his abrasive, if sometimes amusing, comments.

Blundell voiced what must have been in the minds of many – that there was little faith in committees if matters were brought to the Town Council first. This was another indication of the impasse and also of the fact that The Water Question at its present stage, was too big and too crucial to be in the hands of a small number of men. However as Mayfield said, the present state of things was a growing evil and the Committee was fully aware that an alteration was required at once.

So desperate was the situation that Marillier had been instructed to devise a plan to convey water by pipes or carts from the Spring Ditch. From three possibilities offered by Marillier to make the water available, the Committee chose the cheapest – a stand pipe at the end of Prospect Street, supplying 100,000 gallons of drinking water. The Town Council of 9 July, discussed this:

Galloway: Would the standpipe water be free?

Mayfield: Only ratepayers would be allowed to use it. Most people were ratepayers, anyway.

Galloway: It wouldn't solve the problem. Better make a culvert, take the water to Stoneferry and make a mixture.

Willows, supporting Galloway: A single standpipe would serve only one district.

Town Clerk: Galloway's idea would need an Act to enable them to cut through the land.

Galloway: Then use pipes.

Samuelson: The inhabitants would be satisfied if they got Springhead water for drinking purposes.

Moss (who had supported the standpipe idea in Committee, but then learned that Simpson had tried it elsewhere and found the water objectionable): Better continue the experiments, which they could at any time stop, instead of incurring any more expense.

Harrison: Standpipes would not be a short term measure. They would be there for, say, 2½ to 3 years, the time needed for the improvement of the present supply.

. . . And so on, and on . . .

'GOOD, SOLID WATER'

Then Cllr. Richardson, amid laughter, said he opposed all the amendments; 'He had quite sufficient of Mr. Simpson (hear) and would throw him off that very day and take Mr. Warden's offer because he would give them the water and would not ask a farthing until he had secured a supply and only then ask them for £500.

Moss: What of the expense?

Richardson: He will bear the expense himself.

Moss: That is a mis-statement.'

Then Richardson explained that there were parties in the Council who had seen Warden and would vouch for the facts he had just stated. There was further talk and Warden's letter was re-read. Assured by Richardson that Warden would charge no more than £500, another amendment was put forward – to get rid of Simpson and Baker and try local talent. Eventually all the amendments were lost and the Waterworks Committee minutes were confirmed as they stood.

The meeting was, however, adjourned and reconvened on 23 July, 1858. Mayfield wanted to go through the whole business again, even though nothing had changed. He gave a lucid account of the history of the Springhead operation. His own preference was for the spring water, but if that was insufficient, the West Beck. In any case something must be done.

Atkinson said that, to use a vulgar expression, the Waterworks Committee had got to the end of its tether; this was clear from the account Mayfield had given. Atkinson said they had not only got as far as they could themselves, but they had got to the end with Mr. Simpson, 'who only gave one decided opinion in all the communication they had with him.' Atkinson himself was satisfied with the river water, but as many water consumers were not and as they paid the piper, they had the right to call the tune. He moved that the Committee provide estimates for obtaining supplies of 7½ and 10 million gallons a day from near Hull Bridge.

Richardson said he had seen Warden, confirmed the terms of his offer and therefore moved it be accepted. This was seconded

Portrait of Cllr. (later Ald.) Thomas Jackson in the Guildhall.
Photograph: Mr. A. McTurk.

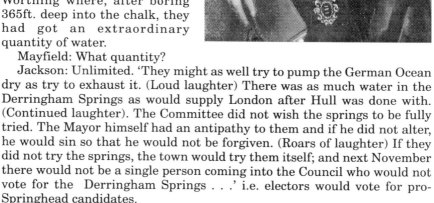

by Wilcox. Jackson, in support: He believed himself – and he had the best of information – that there was 40 foot deep of solid water in a chalk basin for miles and miles.

Mayfield: Do you mean a reservoir?

Jackson: 'Yes, Sir, I mean 40ft. of good solid water in a reservoir in the chalk.' He mentioned Worthing where, after boring 365ft. deep into the chalk, they had got an extraordinary quantity of water.

Mayfield: What quantity?

Jackson: Unlimited. 'They might as well try to pump the German Ocean dry as try to exhaust it. (Loud laughter) There was as much water in the Derringham Springs as would supply London after Hull was done with. (Continued laughter). The Committee did not wish the springs to be fully tried. The Mayor himself had an antipathy to them and if he did not alter, he would sin so that he would not be forgiven. (Roars of laughter) If they did not try the springs, the town would try them itself; and next November there would not be a single person coming into the Council who would not vote for the Derringham Springs . . .' i.e. electors would vote for pro-Springhead candidates.

Gresham supported because he had faith: 'There was plenty of water to be got from the Derringham Springs and there was even as much oozed out at Hessle as would supply Hull'.

Jackson: 'There is no doubt of it and it causes Hessle Whelps'. (Loud and continued laughter).

Mr. Mayfield said the engagement with Mr. Simpson was at an end. Richardson's amendment was carried by a large majority.

Reading the account of this protracted meeting as reported in the *Advertiser*, 10 and 27 July, 1858, one has the impression of total frustration at the start, the Council divided into factions, none with a clear majority, none prepared to give way. The laughter and continued laughter was probably of relief that a way out of the impasse had been offered, which would at least give a different focus if not a complete solution. Mistrust of engineers from London was voiced by Galloway in a Board of Health meeting in early July – 'they'd seen enough of what that course of action could do' – and many of the Councillors would feel better with a local man in charge. The manner of Richardson's opposition to all amendments had been enough to cause a laugh, and even though there was gossip and lobbying before the meeting reconvened to its final phase, it was this point of release that changed the whole situation.

So those 'who would drink vinegar if it came from Springhead' were able to look forward to a spring water supply, now in the hands of William Warden.

1858-9 WARDEN AT SPRINGHEAD

The first phase of Warden's trial at Springhead followed the Council meeting of 24 July, 1858. The total expense of Simpson's efforts had been reported as £1022.8d and the *Advertiser* of 7 August was less than hopeful of Warden's success. 'There is not much confidence expressed that the plan now adopted on the no cure, no pay principle will be any more successful than the last was; and no little anxiety is shown that the Council should not allow itself to depart in the least from the simple proposition upon which this last trial was permitted. Not a penny must be spent, not a liability incurred, until the water is there.' Simpson was quite correct in saying that they still did not know enough about the springs; no-one, not even Warden himself, knew exactly what would be entailed. So little faith was publicly expressed about the experiment (except by the pro-Springhead group who had said the same things all along) that the idea arose of a subscription fund to finance Warden's efforts, for those who said there was a town's water supply at Springhead to 'put their money where their mouth was', as we should commonly say today. It is not clear if this fund ever came into being; certainly it was not mentioned in any of the press accounts of the financial side of the matter, when they became important news later on. Warden did not begin the task immediately. There was a contract to be drawn up, satisfactory to both parties. Through Mr. Mayfield the Waterworks Committee kept on saying they wanted to treat Warden fairly, but Warden and Summers, his solicitor, hung on until the agreement appeared to cover all major eventualities. Agreement was reached by 20 September, 1858, and the following points were covered:

That Warden undertook not to interfere with the present springs (from now on they were more often called the Old Springs);

He would provide spring water good enough for domestic purposes, but would not promise that it would be equal to the present spring water;

He insisted on a right of road over Mr. Walker's land, or every effort on the part of the Corporation to get it;

He claimed to use all the materials then at Springhead, free of charge;

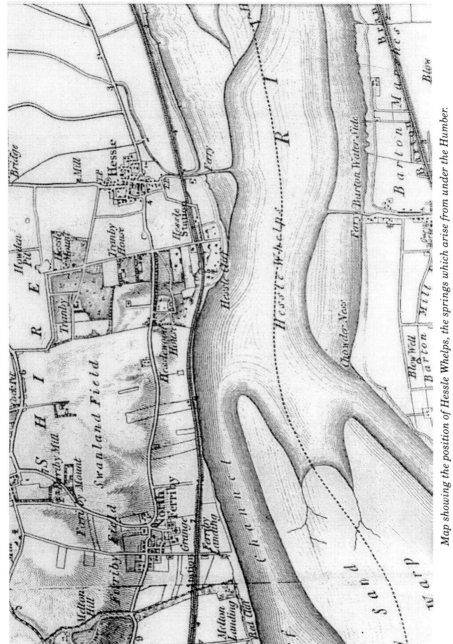

Map showing the position of Hessle Whelps, the springs which arise from under the Humber.

From Victorian Ordanance Survey Map No. 23, published by David and Charles at £3.95.

and also to use the ditch at the west end of the springs to carry away pumped water.

The Town Council agreed, even to helping to get the right of road, but the Town Clerk said of Walker, 'I doubt if he will allow it on any terms'.

Since work had not begun straight away, coals and a pump were carted off from Springhead in the first week of October. Cllr. Jackson, strongly partisan and vociferous in favour of Warden, brought this to the notice of the Waterworks Committee. Mayfield said the pump was needed at Stoneferry and the coals were being wasted. Warden had not by that time (16 October) signed the contract, nor was it known when he would, so the materials were removed, with the earnest promise from Mayfield that Warden would have everything he needed when he started. One can almost read '*if* he started' in the press account of Mayfield's reply.

The right of road was obtained from Mr. Walker at the cost of £30, a sum quoted many times afterwards almost as thirty pieces of silver, when it seemed that Warden's promise was not going to be fulfilled.

In hindsight we can see subtle changes of ideas: Dr. Horner who had spoken of the 'fungus' to be seen by microscopic examination of some waters; the occasional small items about Artesian wells in the papers over the years during which the Water Question had been important in Hull (for example, both 1844, the 290ft. bore to supply the Middlesex Pauper Lunatic Asylum in Hanwell, and the use of Artesian bores for the Trafalgar Square fountains); Mr. Jackson citing Worthing's deep bore of 365ft. yielding unlimited amounts of water. Together Hull's answers were there – deep bores instead of comparatively shallow wells or river water, and testing by looking at the biological content instead of the chemical. Implications of cost were there, too, and the most open-minded by now realised that a pure ample water supply was worth all that would have to be paid for it. People's ideas had been widened about what improvements such a supply would allow. Ample water flushing regularly through the drains would remove some of the smells inherent in the town, personal and domestic cleanliness would prevent many ailments that had been so common, as well as giving a sense of well-being. The 1851 repeal of the window-tax was part of the health campaign, not just from the Board of Health, but part of a wider and growing appreciation of the values of cleanliness and fresh air. It was no accident that as Warden was working at Springhead, plans were afoot for a People's Park as an open amenity within walking distance of the more crowded districts, and for the Model Dwellings in Midland Street to provide comfortable, well-ventilated homes for working people.

Warden seems to have been determined to assert and retain his independence of the Corporation. He had to rely on their help for the right of road, but by the third week of November when this right was sealed and Richardson asked what was going on at Springhead, Mayfield's reply, somewhat sour and disgruntled, was to the effect that Richardson had better ask Warden himself as he had seven months for the experiments and was going to carry on in his own way without Town Council or other interference. Mayfield understood Warden had made one or two bores, but was not in on the secret of his operations.

SLIGHT DIVERSION

Advertiser, 20 November, 1858:

'A highly respectable firm have recently made a 2ins. bore on their premises in North Street and a plentiful flow of beautiful water is the result. The sequence is natural. There is good water for boring in North Street; there must be good water for boring at Stoneferry. Therefore we ought to bore for it at that place. The syllogism is too good. Why should not every house have its own bore?'

The idea of a bore at Stoneferry was already before the Town Council. George Wilkinson had asked for a £100 grant for a test bore there on the principle that the works and distribution system were already in place and should there be a Stoneferry Artesian supply, pipage from Springhead would be unnecessary. By March, 1859, this bore was down 130ft, with £25 of the £100 spent, but Marillier, questioned by Thompson, said there was a great difference between the Springhead water and that from the Stoneferry bore. At the end of April the bore had reached 226ft. and a very hard rock resistant to the tools. There was about £3 or £4 left of the grant and as the water was as useless as ever, this experiment was abandoned as a failure.

WARDEN STILL AT SPRINGHEAD

The Waterworks Committee and the Council were irritated by Warden's independent manner and once again Marillier became, not exactly the liaison, but rather the informant, carrying news of Warden's doings to the Committee. In the first of his reports, Marillier said that Warden was sinking a shaft of 13ft. diameter and had got to a depth of 17ft. This was just before Christmas, 1858.

In the early part of 1859, reporters were allowed into Committee meetings for the first time and far from opening a window to some fresh air, this brought a whirlwind of acrimony into the faces of the newspaper readers. Where before, Committee minutes were presented to the Town Council and not always printed in full, the public was now virtually able to witness what went on in committees and found it to be at least as nasty as what often transpired in the full Council. Long sessions were wasted in arguing the open committee procedure, even after it had been formally decided upon. Tempers were raised, personalities crudely dissected and as a result, true business suffered.

On 24 January, 1859, Marillier visited Springhead and found that the shaft was now 25ft. deep, the chalk had been reached and some 6 inch bores were to be made at the bottom of the shaft. On 16 March, Warden reported by letter to the Committee, sending a copy to the *Eastern Counties Herald* for insertion in the paper. The public was thus informed directly. He had made two bores of 64ft depth, each of which penetrated 40ft into the chalk. Water samples, analysed by Mr. Sollitt, were of 'exceeding purity'. A shaft of 15ft. diameter was then sunk and lined with cement and dry brickwork, but one side of it gave way as they entered the chalk, so 'a nine inch brickwork, laid in Portland cement' was begun and continued up to the surface. Five bores of 6-inch diameter were made from the bottom of this shaft varying in depth from 60 to 90ft into the chalk; they produced 'an overflowing spring of the purest water.' The well could be emptied in about four hours when a 12-inch double acting pump was fixed and working at 45-50 strokes a minute; 'the water was still flowing in considerable quantities from the bores, but not sufficiently strong to keep the pumps going at that rate.' The Old Springs were not affected.

Then came the rub.

Warden had spent a great deal and had had some heavy losses in business and otherwise (it was a period of general recession) and he did not feel he could carry on to a satisfactory conclusion without some financial help. He was still completely confident that the outcome *would* be satisfactory.

The Committee's response was swift and sure:

Eastern Counties Herald, 17 March. 1859, copy of Waterworks Committee resolution –

> 'Resolved, That Mr. Warden be informed that his communication and analysis have been received by this Committee and, considering the mode for defraying the expenses of conducting the experiments and the payment to Mr. Warden if successful have been defined and determined by the stipulations of an agreement entered into by the Town Council and Mr. Warden, this Committee is not at liberty to depart from the provisions of such agreement, *nor can they recommend the Council to depart therefrom.*' (My italics)

Warden's first contract ended 20 April, 1859.

An action group called the Town's Water Committee came into being about this time. Its leading light was Mr. John Jaques Matthewson, of 9 Junction Street, a cabinet maker and restorer of old paintings. A meeting was held at his premises on 30 April, 1859; Mr. Fullam of the South Myton Reform Association and always a strong supporter of the Springhead group, being in the chair. He spoke of the unwholesomeness of the Stoneferry water and besides mentioning the Beverley sewage, told of 'three persons, being drowned, who had drifted backwards and forwards from Hull to Beverley before they were found.' However, at this meeting it was the Committee, rather than the water itself, which came in for the most condemnation and a resolution was framed that sufficient money be granted to enable Mr. Warden to test the springs thoroughly. The following evening, another meeting was held at which a memo. was adopted, requesting the Council to assist Warden in a thorough test of the springs. This memo. was distributed to various shops in the town where people could sign it before it was presented on 14 April.

As the *Hull Free Press*, which reported these doings. said, 'What we complain of is a want of sincerity on the part of our Waterworks Committee in their pretended efforts to get us better water . . . Money has been spent time after time repeating experiments that never could be called tests . . . Mr. Warden is the only man who has gone to the task with a determination to accomplish it and we sincerely hope that the independent members of the Council and the public will not see him with his work half finished.'

WHAT WAS BEING TESTED?

Both Wicksteed and Simpson had tested the capacity of the springs only, by pumping from the basin of the springs.

Early in 1858, it had become apparent to some observers that Simpson's experiment was already a failure. On 13 March, 1858, the *Hull Free Press* put the situation in straight-forward terms: 'When we last visited Derringham we saw three indifferent pumps sucking in three different puddles. Only one of the pumps acted with any degree of efficiency. The centrifugal pump was idle and the two common pumps to the west of the centrifugal one were worse than idle, for although working, they were not lifting any water; while of the water lifted by the one efficient pump, a full third was permitted to run back again into the basin of the springs. The complexion of the fluid pumped was that of the Humber at high tide and the appearance of the springs was of three half-dried puddles . . . the whole affair wears a very lame and bungling aspect.' So much for Simpson's test.

What are they testing? asked the writer, at that time. It was well known there was good water at Derringham and therefore there should be bores made around the springs, continued the article. This was a shift of opinion from this paper and closer to Oldham's ideas. Eighteen months later, on 29 September, 1860, H. J. Whiting wrote a long letter to the *Hull Free Press:*

'I can never believe that when Wicksteed and Simpson told us that not more than one million gallons per day could be got from Springhead that they were so ignorant of their business that they knew no better . . . If these men believed in their own tests, they proved themselves totally unfit for the high positions they occupy – if not, why was such a piece of deception practised upon the people of Hull?'

The dealings with Warden were half-hearted at best, obstructive at worst.

Few had really taken in what he had communicated. He had written to Mayfield at length before his offer of 24 March, 1858, and in this first letter had made the wisest comment of anyone to date:

'THE FRESH COMING DOWN THE RIVER HULL AND THE SPRINGHEAD WATER ARE BOTH FROM ONE GREAT SOURCE; BY TAKING WATER FROM THE SPRING YOU GET IT PURELY FILTERED FROM THE GREAT NATURAL STREAM IN ITS COURSE TO THE HUMBER, THROUGH THE GRAVEL AND THE FISSURES IN THE CHALK STONE; BY TAKING IT FROM THE RIVER YOU GET IT IMPREGNATED WITH ALL KINDS OF FILTH.'

Even he did not realise the magnitude of the task. Eccles, in his account, said Warden had apparently expected to get water by merely sinking a well. He was quite satisfied that no power that could be brought could exhaust the springs, 'provided the pipes are put into the springs 12-15 feet from the present level.'

Jackson, whose 'forty foot of solid water' had incurred derision, was nearest to the solution when he cited the deep Artesian bore at Worthing. George Wilkinson, also, whose idea it had been to bore at Stoneferry, was near to the correct idea; it was unfortunate that the water obtained was useless when the money ran out, as an even deeper bore there could possibly have yielded the desired result with the established works in close proximity.

Warden had had several hitches in the provision of water for the railway company at Hessle Station and although he had specified 12-15ft into the chalk at Springhead, he realised that greater depth might ultimately be needed, for he said later that the Hessle experience had led him to the conclusion that they could get any quantity of water BY GOING DEEP ENOUGH FOR IT. It seems strange, therefore that 12-15ft was specified for Springhead, unless this was intended to make believe to an impatient Council that the task would be accomplished in a short time and without a hint of extra cost,

It is not clear from the newspaper reports if Warden's first letter ever came before the Waterworks Committee. Perhaps it was passed over quickly as just another bit of native talent trying to make its mark and not receiving the consideration it deserved.

The summer of 1858 dragged on, nobody seeming to know what it were best to do. The Town Council and, indeed, the Waterworks Committee did not know what Warden's real intentions were. Predictions in the *Hull Free Press* were as gloomy as those in the *Advertiser*. The *Herald* said little or nothing, except to pour scorn on the suggestion of going to the Driffield Springs – why go so far away, when springs there are, bubbling up in the fields between Beverley Parks and Hessle, the Kell-gate Spring in Cottingham being a noted example?

WARDEN AT SPRINGHEAD, PHASE TWO

Of all the accounts of this stage of the proceedings, after a second contract between Warden and the Corporation in July, 1859, the short, sharp facts appearing in the *Hull Free Press* each Saturday, were the easiest to follow Starting about Christmas, 1859, they succinctly charted Warden's progress from confusion to a partial success. The reporter was Matthewson himself. He visited the works daily to help and encourage Warden and on Fridays made his report to the paper.

17 Dec 1859	Except for three tons of it, all the boring machinery is at Springhead and being set up.
24 Dec	Three more loads of boring machinery arrived. Have had ten days severe weather, with 13 to 17 degrees (F) of frost, but work continued early and late.
31 Dec	All machinery fixed and fitted. Boring will begin at once.
7 Jan. 1860	Boring commenced Thursday noon (5 Jan.). Greatest precision and effect. A bore of 16ins. diameter already 10ft into chalk and through a layer of flint 13ins. thick.
14 Jan.	20ft into chalk, nearly all layers of flints, some of great thickness.
28 Jan.	Rubbly nature of the chalk and the vast quantity of flint now being mastered. Hole must be lined for several feet with iron tubing.
4 Feb.	Preparation of the bore-hole for the iron tubing. Chalk, soft and water-saturated, fallen into the hole.
11 Feb.	Three tons of tubing arrived from Manchester. Boring proceeding, 50ft. deep, water flowing with great force.
18 Feb.	12 more feet of tubing fixed. Strong flow of water presented great obstruction, especially that flowing between chalk and outside of tube. Depth of bore, 64ft.
25 Feb.	Boring through a succession of flint beds from 3 to 15ins. thick. Resistance of flint has broken several cutting irons. Water flowing with great force. Iron tube is 18ins. proud of the surface and water rising up and over it 'assumes the form of a glass shade through which the iron tube is seen.'
3 Mar	Very thick flint beds. Water flows up with greater force as the bore deepens. Now 150ft. Severely cold weather – machines covered with beautiful icicles.
10 Mar	Boring progressing; more water with more depth.
17 Mar	Depth of bore 186ft. Tues., 9 p.m. flint penetrated and water rushed up with great force. Another flint broached. Wed. 10 p.m. 'and the water immediately following takes on the appearance, on falling over the tube top, of the segment of a

	sphere, about 4ft 6ins. in diameter'. Spring Ditch more full than ever seen. Outlet near old Botanic Waterworks to be made larger to prevent flooding of fields.
24 Mar	AS A MATTER OF SCIENCE, THE WATER QUESTION MAY NOW BE LOOKED UPON AS SETTLED.
31 Mar	Depth 228ft, increased flow. Operations will continue next week and then machinery moved to make another bore about 30ft west of the present one.

By 19 May, 1860, the second bore was 100ft. deep and water was flowing. On 4 August, with the bore at 225 ft, the water was flowing with tremendous force. At the end of September, when official trial was made of the amount of water to be obtained from Springhead, the first bore was 252ft. deep, the second, 440ft.

A MEETING UNDER THE TREES

During the summer of 1860, there was growing anticipation of a very successful result at Springhead, giving more water than anyone had expected.

A sub-committee had been formed to report on the work at the springs. Variously called the Derringham Springs Committee or Waterworks Committee No. 2, it comprised Gresham (chairman), Field, Dowsing, Galloway, Chapman and Eccles. No. 2 Committee was without power except via the main committee and the Town Council, and seemed much more inclined to report progress than setbacks. During 1859, especially, when the Water Question reached the full Council, discussion became heated and more than once meetings were adjourned to avoid further argument or action being taken. The Derringham Springs Committee visited the works occasionally; sometimes Gresham went alone. The Town's Water Committee and the newspapers gave the Council information about the strong feelings of some Hull people, but the pressure group was disappointed in the lack of commitment on the part of most inhabitants.

Reporters and Councillors continued to visit the Springhead works during 1860 and after the more powerful machinery was installed, real progress became apparent. To view the works, an omnibus carried interested people for the fare of one shilling (5p) return from King William in the Market Place. The fossils that were brought up from the bore were interesting, but the appearance, each time a flint was broken through, of more and more water, flowing with great force and filling the Spring Ditch to overflowing, was even more exciting. People went to the ditch for their water if it was not too far from home, and no doubt some of the water carts were filled directly from it, instead of taking water via the stand pipe.

Even in the second phase of his operations, Warden had been hindered because of the road over Walker's land. At the time of the second contract, July 1859, nothing was done to renew the right of way because it was fine weather and the road along the Spring Ditch could be used; but on 31 December, 1859, the last two ton load of machinery arrived at the lane to the springs to find the gate locked 'By Order', and the load had to be carted round by Anlaby village and then over swarthland (grassland, probably grazed by sheep) and ploughed fields, a considerable detour entailing time and expense, especially as there was a drain to be crossed, over which a temporary bridge had to be thrown. The weather was bad, with severe frost and snow; it had been a white Christmas.

Still the effort was worthwhile, as with better machinery the water really began to flood out. As early as 10 March, 1860, after Mr. Sollitt's favourable analysis, the *Hull Free Press* observed, 'The only part of the question remaining to be settled is the quantity and it may as safely be asserted that the quantity is no more a question of doubt than the quality was before.' Jackson, in Council, said there was an immense quantity of water flowing 'sparkling with life,' an expression causing laughter in the meeting.

It was not until September that the two pumps were delivered to test the amount that could be obtained from Springhead. Once these were fixed, Gresham went to see, and in Mr. Warden's absence, spoke to Mr. Harrop, the man in charge, who said that the enormous quantity then flowing was amounting to about 3½ million gallons per day, but if perfect engines and better pumps were used, he believed 6 mgpd could be obtained without exhausting the bores. Up-to-date equipment was being employed – a Palmer's rotary hydraulic pump, an invention patented in the United States in 1857 and in some European countries, including Britain, in 1858. It was working well within its capacity, as although able to lift 20 mgpd, it was being used at half speed and the outlet was partly plugged with pieces of wood. The Derringham Springs Committee, on a visit during September, judged that more than double the town's needs could be met when they saw the tremendous flow of water. After their visit they held an impromptu meeting under the trees of a nearby field, in order to fix the day on which a public trial could take place. They expected thousands of people to come, so there would be a band to add to the feeling of festivity. The Committee would entertain Mr. Warden to dinner at their own expense.

The test started on Wednesday, 26 September 1860 and finished the next day. Public notices in the press gave the results.

WARDEN: 'I have now worked the pump 24 hours, having commenced yesterday at 20 minutes to 2 o'clock and ceased today at 20 minutes past 4 o'clock. The difference of time of commencement and finishing was in consequence of a leakage in the boiler and heavy rain during the night, which caused the belt to slip. During the 24 hours, according to a mathematical calculation which has been made, the quantity of water discharged by the pump amounts to

6,021,000 gallons

The result must be eminently satisfactory, especially when we consider that during the whole of the time we could not lower the bores more than 5ft 11ins. The quantity to be raised, is, therefore, merely a question of power. The water has been analysed and found to be of remarkable purity. The town, therefore, is now in possession of an abundant supply of pure wholesome water.'

There were, as expected vast crowds at Springhead, with banners flying and the Druids' band playing. At 6 p.m. at the Vittoria hotel near the Pier (a usual venue for such gatherings) a self-congratulatory company sat down to dine. There followed speeches by and toasts to Mr. Warden, Mr. Matthewson and Cllr. Jackson. On the same day H. J. Whiting published a long letter in the *Hull Free Press* condemnatory of No.1 Waterworks Committee and denouncing Wicksteed's and Simpson's tests as humbug.

At Springhead in the afternoon, there was great curiosity and amusement to see what Cllr. Percival Lambert would do, for as a long-time sceptic he had vowed to drink all that was produced over five million gallons. He would have had a problem for

Mr. MARILLIER's result of the test, in the press immediately after Warden's result, was given in the following statement:

'I find that the total quantity is –

2,724,912 gallons.

In the 24 hours of pumping, the maximum at any one time, for a few minutes, 3,610,800 gallons.'

Well, well; an intriguing paradox.

REVELATIONS AND RECRIMINATIONS

The end of Warden's first contract was 20 April, 1859.

At the 7 April meeting of the Waterworks Committee there was talk about the situation and Mayfield would have moved that Simpson be recalled, had not the Town Clerk reminded him of the imminence of the end of the contract and suggested the resolution be postponed. Cllr. Jackson had a not uncharacteristic outburst at this point, aimed at Mr. Mayfield, 'I think, Mr. Chairman, you have treated the thing unharshly (*sic*), unfairly, ungentlemanly, unmanly. You have said everything against everything and everything against this man.' The Mayor, interrupting, thought Mr. Jackson was joking when he made such serious charges against the Chairman; Mr. Brownlow thought it was said to amuse the reporters. Jackson wanted to vote another £100 for Warden to continue, but when the Mayor asked what guarantee there was that Mr. Warden would do another stroke of work if he were handed such a sum, even Jackson had to admit it was a point worth pondering.

Various well-attended meetings were held in the town by the pro-Springhead partisans, especially the Town's Water Committee. On 4 June, 1859, the *Advertiser* said, 'The Water Question is interminable . . . The Town Council is in this position – they have done all they could to test the springs and the result is the conviction that they will not yield the required supply of water . . . they cannot be justified in spending any more of the public money on further experiments.' However, that week's meeting of the Waterworks Committee included the following surprising statement from Ald. Bannister: he was giving notice he would move at the next Council meeting that Warden be allowed the use of the springs for three months more.

Blundell had spoken of 16 months waste of time.

Percival Lambert had reiterated his belief that Warden would fail.

Mayfield, of course, was all for Simpson's return.

Dowsing and Eccles had moved and seconded that the debate be adjourned, a resolution that was carried.

And yet, after all this, when the Town Clerk was asked if Warden should give up the ground at Springhead, Bannister had prevented a reply with his remarkable announcement.

Why?

The answer did not appear in any of the papers at the time, but was revealed in a series of letters to the *Eastern Morning News,* some years later.

Anthony Bannister believed that a source higher up the river would eventually be the solution, but he was one of a group supporting Warden in his efforts to test the springs, once and for all. Although Warden's contract was running out, Bannister felt more could be done.

J. J. Matthewson was the real energy behind the publicity and pressure groups and in this instance he said he would call an open meeting, to be held in the large room behind his shop. He published circulars advertising the meeting, to be held on the Friday evening. It was intended to rouse the public at large in the great enterprise of seeking an ample, pure water supply. Matthewson told Eccles of the meeting, but Eccles was unfortunately to be out of town at the time. However the meeting was reported in the *Hull Free Press* on the Saturday and on Monday, Eccles asked Matthewson more about it, The report said that at this 'influential' meeting 'resolutions were unanimously carried advocating the continuance of Mr. Warden's experiments at Springhead and the grant of a further extension of time by the Corporation.'

Eccles then suggested that Ald. Bannister should put it to the Council that three months' extension should be given. Because Matthewson's meeting showed there was public support, this was done, the extension granted and Warden was able to go on to phase two.

Eccles asked Matthewson if many people had been at the Friday night meeting.

Matthewson: 'Oh, it was most "influential".'

Eccles then went through the names of a large number of people to whom he knew Matthewson would have sent a circular, 'and singular to relate, most of them had had . . . *bona fide* excuses for non-attendance.'

Eccles: 'Who the Dickens, then, were present?'

He replied, 'I know, Eccles, you won't split, so I don't mind telling you; there was not a soul came to the meeting, so I proposed myself into the chair; I put the resolutions (which I had previously carefully prepared) to the meeting and they were carried unanimously, I then wrote out the reports of the proceedings and took myself to the printing office in Bowlalley lane, and, as I was not going to trust even Mr. Whiting, the proprietor, to insert it without my first seeing a proof, I waited till 1.30 a.m. on Saturday to see a correct proof of it and then went home and slept comfortably!'

(Quoted from Eccles' letter to the *Eastern Morning News,* 29 Aug. 1898.

Curiously, I have not been able to find the article by Matthewson (marked 'Communicated') in the *Hull Free Press.*

J. J. Matthewson played a vital part in Warden's activities at Springhead. He was a very knowledgeable geologist, aware of the problems that could arise and on many difficult occasions it was only because Matthewson urged Warden to continue that the work progressed. In the long argumentative Council meetings to settle Warden's accounts, Matthewson was always mentioned with favour and gratitude even by those who were hardest upon Warden. It was generally acknowledged that without Matthewson behind him and, indeed, working beside him at the Springs, Warden would not have got as far as he did. As Martin Samuelson put it later, 'Warden never knew what he was about, but he had a man in the town by whose orders he worked . . .'

Warden's first contract had stipulated a payment of £500 only if he produced 5 million gallons of water per day for a test period of 30 days. The total time the operations were to take was not stated; all the indications are that Warden expected it to be a few months at most. When this contract ended, the Council were slow in doing anything about it, even after a reminder from the Town Clerk. The second phase, starting as it did in the summer when tracks were passable, was begun without any recourse to Mr. Walker to obtain or extend the right of way to the springs. Again, Warden may have thought he was not going to be long. There was fault on both sides. Mr. Summers, Warden's solicitor, is not reported as making any overtures about the right of way, nor did the Town Clerk, who was normally on the alert if any matter touched upon the Corporation.

It was revealed by John Gresham in another debate that, although it had been said in late 1859 that Warden did not order boring apparatus because he didn't know he was going to get an extension of time, in fact he had tried to get the machinery. Gresham said, 'A new invention for boring was discovered by a firm in Manchester. Mr. Warden consequently entered into an arrangement with the inventor of this machinery, but so great was the demand for it in the country that a great deal of time was lost before it was procured.'

That took up to Christmas, 1859, and by then a very severe winter had set in during which, well into 1860, thirteen fires were kept burning 'to prevent the men from starving'. The coal bill therefore mounted up to £100. This insight, from Cllr. Dawson, was one of the very, very few about the difficulties under which the men worked.

Matthewson's business suffered, as he was at Springhead more than at his shop. Great theoretical knowledge of the area, allied to this practical experience, gave authority to his 'Facts and figures from Springhead' appearing weekly in the *Free Press*. It seems that after the disappointment of the first phase, Warden became sceptical, as the bores went deeper and deeper, encountering hard and difficult flint beds on the way, without the desired result, but Matthewson's bolstering encouragement made him realise that he, William Warden, could become the sole provider of Hull's new water supply.

Finding that Matthewson was right and he was sure to get the water, he 'shirked his acquaintance' to take all the credit for himself, as the *Free Press* put it on 9 February, 1861.

Warden had also said to Matthewson, before they split up, 'It would pay us to stand with the other party,' to which Matthewson replied, 'But they don't want the water.' Warden: 'Ah, well, never mind, but it would pay us better.'

This story appeared more than once in the papers in different guises and was quoted in Council. It is impossible to tell where it originated or if it were true, but certainty the *Free Press* (from 12 January, 1861, called *Holiday's Free Press*, under a new proprietor) which had styled itself the champion of the Springhead experiments, had by then done a complete *volte face* on Warden and even on the belief of the adequacy of the Springhead supply.

Ald. Mayfield said more than once that he wished they had never let Warden interfere.

The Council were in difficulties, though. The Stoneferry water was still 'foul', 'filthy', 'obnoxious' and so on and there were also some distribution problems.

Reports of the disastrous fire at the Theatre Royal in Wellington Street on the morning of 14 October, 1859, describe the fire and the fire-fighting very vividly, but also show that the water was turned off from the service pipes in the evenings, so that during the night there was water in the mains only, serving standpipes in case of fire. The turncocks went round at 6 a.m. and turned on the service pipes to allow the normal daily supply, but this fire was first noted at 7.15 a.m. – a time when not only was the water not confined to the standpipes, but was also in general use. The turncocks had to be found to turn the water off again, so that there was enough pressure for the hoses.

Without the service pipes connected, there was supposed to be enough pressure in the mains to throw water to a height of 150-160 feet. Mr. Marillier had warned the Waterworks Committee several times in past years that there was not enough power in the Stoneferry engines. On 28 June, 1859, there had been an accident to the large engine, but it was working again within 33 hours of breaking down. During that time the two small engines were mostly working together, but when there was only one, there was scarcely enough pressure to force water into the town. The usual practice had been to use the large engine for normal supply, boosted by one of the smaller ones on Saturdays. From the time of the accident, the boost was added on Wednesdays as well.

Cllr. Jackson said in Committee that this showed the need for more engine power; Ald. Thompson said this had long ago been pointed out to the Council, but these suggestions were set aside. Marillier gave evidence to the Waterworks Committee, reported in the *Herald* on 21 July, 1859. He said a new engine should have a cylinder of at least 85ins. diameter against the 75ins. of the present one, to give a third more power and, if required, be able to deliver 4 million gallons per day. Marillier also said that this engine could be used whatever the source of the water, as his opinion was that the Stoneferry works should be retained as a means of distribution to the town. His estimated cost of the Stoneferry improvements was about £13,000, which would have been less when the matter was raised before. With the usual formalities this work was started, while Warden continued to labour at Springhead.

REMUNERATION

As has been seen, work continued at the springs until the 24-hour test in September, 1860. The huge discrepancy between Marillier's and Warden's results caused some embarrassment to the Derringham Springs Committee, for they were in a dilemma how to present the official report. Warden, called into the Committee meeting of 1 October, was convinced of his accuracy – and yet, although he had calculated the flow to be 6,300,000 gallons, a 'friend of considerable ability' (Matthewson, presumably) had reached a figure 200,000 gallons less and so, rather than overstate, he had published the friend's result. The leaky state of the engine in which 'they had been unable to raise steam sufficiently to carry on the operation with vigour' had possibly reduced the amount from what could have been obtained, he said.

Marillier persisted with the accuracy of *his* report; that they had not reached 3 million gallons that day. It was decided that the Town Clerk should engage a disinterested umpire, and at the Committee meeting on 31 October, Thorp (the Borough Surveyor), Marillier and Warden attended. Mr. Thorp, said the two tanks for a further test would be ready the next day. Each held

3,000 gallons and had been tried already, filling one of them in 50 seconds. Warden had worked 'diligently' since the last, inconclusive test and a boiler was on its way from Messrs Clayton and Shuttleworth's factory. 'All he had to complain of was that the town had not rendered him adequate monetary assistance in carrying out his expensive project.' At the test on the following Monday, watched critically by many people, including the Mayor, Ald. W. Hodge, it was 'generally agreed' that the flow was greater than 3,000 galls/min. and two days later the Derringham Springs Committee resolved that Warden should name the day for the start of a 6-day test.

The figures from this test in the *Advertiser*'s Supplementary Sheet of 12 January, 1861, indicate two different methods of working. Marillier gave results for 5 days, but for some reason not stated, was not prepared to publish the 6th day's figure. His method seemed to be to measure the contents of the tank each time. Warden merely multiplied the number of tanks filled by 3,000 to give the number of gallons yielded each day. In general, therefore, Warden's figures were higher than Marillier's but all were around the 4¼ million gallon mark. Marillier still believed the 30-day test should be done as the level of the springs could fall. 1860 had been a year of 'unexampled rain' and the springs just then were flowing freely. Still, as Gresham said at the next Town Council meeting, Warden had got more than anyone expected; even Marillier had said to him, in the Mayor's presence, that if Warden got 4 million gallons a day he would be satisfied and so no doubt would the Corporation.

By January, 1861, the exact yield of water was an almost secondary consideration to the Council, for there was plenty of water for everyone to see, but – WARDEN WAS ASKING FOR MONEY!

For eight months, until the end of August, 1861, the question of how to settle with Warden occupied major parts of Town Council and Waterworks Committee meetings. Every shade of opinion was held among the 56 Councillors; every nuance was expressed. There were contradictions, changes of view, the raking up of old ideas and Ald. Thompson firmly holding on to the belief that the Stoneferry Mixture was ample and of as good a quality as anywhere in the country. The *Hull Free Press,* while it was still in a good mood about the Springhead operations (7 April, 1860) had a ditty to Thompson to the tune of *The Last Rose of Summer*:

> 'Tis the last unbeliever, left grumbling alone.
> All his creaking companions have fled him and gone.
> No chum of his kidney, no noodle is nigh
> To believe in Stoneferry, Springhead to descry.

> We'll not leave thee, thou stern one, to fume, fret and swell.
> Since the wise have come over, O come thou as well.
> Thus widely we scatter thy hopes like the spray
> As our bores utter millions of gallons per day.

Soon, soon thou must follow, of friends quite bereft
And with scarce in Committee one old stickler left.
With thy foolish old crotchets all shivered and blown
Why linger in noodledom, why growl on alone?

Thompson was of stern stuff. A long-serving Alderman, a Committee man, he knew the rules and kept to them. He took a long time to become convinced that the Derringham Springs might yield enough water for the town; Bannister remarked in the Council meeting of 18 January, 1861, that the climax of the Waterworks Committee's work was getting Thompson to say there was plenty of water at Springhead. Warden, however, had made a contract: £500, no cure, no pay, and it was no good the *Advertiser* saying 'there is, if not a cure, something like a convalescence'. To Thompson, the contract was a binding agreement, no half measures. So that since Warden had indeed received £500 in two instalments during the later part of the experiment, Thompson considered him very well done to in the circumstances. The *Advertiser*'s leader of 5 January, 1861, considered the question of Warden's remuneration settled because the £500 had been paid: 'However much he may have bungled and prevaricated, still he has got a large supply of water in the end and cannot be allowed to pass unrewarded.' But, apart from the money there was the 30-day trial. Moss chided Gresham as the latter seemed disposed to release Warden from this part of the contract. Early in January, Z. C. Pearson put a long motion which was eventually carried; among its clauses was the expression 'that this Council declares itself satisfied' and Pearson laid on the table another motion for consideration at the next meeting that Warden should be paid further.

Mr. Charles Lambert said no inhabitant of a lunatic asylum could have made a more extravagant proposition.

Warden was claiming expenses totalling £2559.3s.0½d. (£2559.15) Gresham and Dawson had gone through the wages book and found it correct. There were vouchers for £573.4s.3d and there would be a refund from Mather and Platt when the hired machinery was returned. The Derringham Springs Committee resolved that as Warden's demand amounted to £1827 after the machinery refund had been accounted for, they would recommend to the Council that he be paid £1327 over and above the earlier £500.

This came before the full Council on 7 February, 1861. Gresham put the motion, referring to the propriety of giving to Mr. Warden such remuneration as was due to his successful completion of his exertions at Springhead.

Ald. Thompson opposed this with a long and powerful speech. He stressed the details and binding nature of the contract. He very reasonably argued that Warden should have sought the Council's advice when he realised he was overspending the £500 he had been promised for success.

Ald. Atkinson, too, was against paying the sum submitted as he had heard that were it paid it would be used as a lever for a larger sum by way of compensation.

Ald. Bannister was also against the motion, calling Warden's accounts 'gross deception' and stating that Warden, in correspondence, deliberately sought to mislead by citing examples of costs of bores which were not comparing like with like; by comparing Springhead with bores made many years ago when there was no sophisticated boring machinery and by comparing with bores the greater cost of which had included permanent pumps. He nevertheless granted the success of Warden's work and therefore put it to the meeting that Warden be paid a further £250. The motion was lost but Atkinson's motion for yet another deferment was carried.

The *Advertiser* confessed on 9 February, 1861, to having been greatly amused with the Town Council's displays of petulant helplessness in the matter of Mr. Warden; 'they are . . . under a kind of misty terror that they will never be able to get rid of him.'

It came out of the arguments before settlement was reached that it was Matthewson who had been instrumental in getting the two payments of £250 before the work was finished, in order that Warden could carry on.

Warden made a foolish move towards the end of March when he wrote to the Waterworks Committee after that body had asked him what he expected to receive. His letter stated unequivocally that he wanted £2,000 for services, above the amount expended. To him the amount expended was a gross figure and higher than Gresham and Dawson had calculated: £2548.16s.0½d. At the same time Warden also wrote to the Town Council a somewhat naive epistle in which he admitted that he realised at the time of the contract that £500 was too little and that £2,000 was nearer the mark. In his simplicity, he said, he thought the Corporation would have paid him £500 long before the work was finished. This is another indication, perhaps, that he had expected the task to show much quicker and more definite results than actually was the case.

Work was going on at Stoneferry and quite large sums being paid for machinery, etc. during 1861. The whole Council should have known by then the importance of a pure water supply in preventing disease for chill reminders of the cholera's presence reappeared every autumn; the most sinister for a port like Hull so close to the Continent, was the great epidemic in Bruges in October 1859, when there were 40 deaths a day, the population of Bruges being 50,000, about half that of Hull. When Warden's account was settled in August, 1861, the *Packet* carried a leader which, although stressing the fact that Warden had no legal claim whatsoever and describing his letter demanding compensation as 'something worse than folly', came down to the real nub of the matter with the question, 'We have paid £70,000 for foul water to be supplied to us; ought we to haggle over a few hundred pounds for a pure supply?'

Gresham, in Pearson's absence, had put the motion that Warden be paid a sum not exceeding £2,500, but it was over-ridden by a resolution to defer the matter again.

Eventually, on 29 August, 1861, an amendment by Capt. Norwood by which Warden had to renounce all claims on the Corporation, granted him £1500 remuneration for his efforts in addition to the original £500.

ENTER THOMAS DALE

29 August, 1861, was an auspicious day. Continued clamour for the Springhead water, had made the building of a waterworks there a foregone conclusion. Expenditure at Stoneferry ensured that those works would not be abandoned for some time and pipes had been laid across the new People's Park in anticipation of conveying the water from Springhead to Stoneferry for distribution. Marillier had been asked to make plans for a waterworks at Springhead, but all of a sudden, he announced his resignation upon being appointed Engineer to the Docks Company.

Advertisements were published and from a candidature of 70, on 29 August, Thomas Dale, the Wakefield Surveyor, was appointed resident engineer for the waterworks.

SPRINGHEAD AND STONEFERRY CONNECTED

Thomas Dale did not let the grass grow under his feet. His first tasks were to acquaint himself with the various waterworks, to look over his predecessor's final report to the Committee and then to come back to the Committee, at Marillier's request, to see if he agreed with what was written. Dale therefore checked the water pipes in the town and found that repairs were necessary in several streets where Marillier had said that none was needed. At the Waterworks Committee requesting more pipes for maintenance during the next six months, he asked for 400 yards, but the Committee granted him double the amount because at that time iron was cheap, but it was also an act of faith in his ability.

As the route the Springhead water should take had been predetermined by the amount of capital recently expended at Stoneferry on the new engine and its housing – some £13,000 – so the state of the filtration system there was forcing a choice. Dale, called in to give his opinion, at first seemed to be favouring more expenditure on the filters, but on 21 November, 1861, he stated that it would be better to set about the Springhead works as soon as possible.

He had already altered Marillier's proposed line of pipes (7,436 yards) from Springhead to Stoneferry. Where Marillier had literally cut corners,

Dale mapped out a longer route (8,272 yards) along public roads, which, although more expensive in piping and awkward because of sharp angles, would be a saving in time, expense and trouble overall, as some of the landowners on Marillier's plan were proving obstinate.

Tenders were sought for various aspects of the work at Springhead. Dale discovered that a 16ft. strip of land along the Spring Ditch belonged to the Corporation. This, he said, could form an ample roadway, but for the transport of materials and coals he suggested a tramway of about 1¼ miles in length from the line of railway crossing the Spring Ditch near the Trinity House Estates (i.e. a line from Dairycoates, northwards to Cottingham). Accordingly, negotiations with the North Eastern Railway Company for rails and engines were started. Marillier had allowed for a natural fall of about 5ft. between Springhead and Stoneferry and therefore a 30ft. lift was required to produce 5 million gallons per day, powered by an engine of 116-120 h.p. Dale said this could be reduced if found too much.

Ald. Thompson began to ask Dale detailed questions in the Waterworks Committee meeting of 26 December, 1861. On enquiring if the engines etc. would be fixed at Springhead before the boring took place, Mr. Mayfield, the Chairman, said that Dale should not be asked questions of that kind at this stage, whereupon Ald. Thompson left the room with the sharp retort, 'Well, well, if I'm not going to get answers to my questions, Good Morning!'

Money was still being spent on incidentals at Stoneferry, for in late November, 1861, the British Gas Light Co. was approached for their terms for installing gas lighting in place of oil lamps. Marillier continued to supervise there as he had undertaken to complete the installation of the new engine and the building of the engine house for £5,500 against a contractor's estimate of £7,600. Richardson asked in Council if Marillier would continue to be paid and Mayfield presumed he would be made some proper compensation for having saved the Corporation so large a sum.

Warden was still alert to the waterworks enterprise, and although it was reported in the *Packet* of 27 September, 1861, that he had been paid the agreed £1,500, he continued to offer suggestions. For example, the same issue of the *Packet* carried a letter from Warden advocating the use of Clark's process, not only to soften the water and thereby save soap, but also, he claimed, the reaction would precipitate a large amount of organic matter. On 13 December, the *Packet*, reporting on the previous day's Town Council meeting, gave the news that all the members, including the Town Clerk, had received a printed letter from Warden, suggesting that, as the Stoneferry plant was established and working, instead of boring at Springhead, they should bore at Stoneferry. 'OBTAIN IT ON THE SPOT' his letter proclaimed. He believed George Wilkinson's idea was perfectly correct, but the bore, at 250ft. had not gone deep enough. Warden thought it would be necessary to go to 500ft. because of the dip in the chalk. (This letter may be seen at Yorkshire Water's Museum). None of his letters sparked any comment or action in Council or Committee. In this case the letter was merely taken as read. They were done with him. Dale was now their man.

£4,000 was borrowed at 4% for the new works, and £100 lodged to the credit of Mr. Dale towards expenses at Springhead. The rails for the tramway were to be supplied by F. & W. Firth of Leeds at £6 a ton; the Kirkstall Forge Co's tender of £6,385 to supply engines at the works and W. & J. Hall's tender to build the engine house, boiler house and cottage for £4,283 were both accepted.

On Monday, 26 January, 1862, the Mayor, Z. C. Pearson, accompanied by several members of the Corporation and others, attended at Stoneferry for the purpose of turning the first sod. 'There was a goodly number of persons present. The spot selected was on a piece of rising ground and was marked with flags, etc.' Dale showed the plan of the line of pipes from Springhead to Stoneferry; Ald. Mayfield, in presenting the ceremonial spade to the Mayor, commented that the Waterworks Committee had every reason to hope that the matter would be completed during his Worship's mayoralty; Pearson 'very cleverly turned the sod,' according to the *Advertiser* and he then made a smoothly placatory speech, referring to all the arguments and acrimony as 'differences of opinion'. He was glad the project was starting when trade was bad as it would give the labouring poor a chance to earn a few shillings. He asked God's blessing, and prayed there would be no accident during the work and 'that everyone engaged in it would have life to carry on.' The official party then adjourned to the lodge where a lunch was provided by the Mayor.

The new Stoneferry engine was set to work permanently at the end of March, 1862. The tramway was then in course of construction and on 18 April the *Advertiser* told its readers that the Waterworks Committee had visited Springhead and due to the 'marvellous rapidity' of the work there, the tramway was already laid.

Because of difficulty in acquiring some land at the Stoneferry end, the pipe-laying there was delayed, so Dale ordered it to be started at Springhead. Water had been diverted from the Spring Ditch to the dyke at the north side of the bank, which had been dug out several feet to take the rush of water. The iron water pipes were supplied by the firm of Bolckow and Vaughan of Middlesbrough and Dale ensured their high quality by having them inspected before leaving the factory and then inspecting them himself on arrival. Faulty sections were sent back. By mid-April, the pipe-laying was so far advanced, about 2½ miles having been laid, that Dale thought he would be able to let the overflow from the springs run through the pipes to Stoneferry about the middle of July. At the end of May the Old Springs had been pumped out and a part of them arched over. Both engine house and boiler house were rapidly nearing completion. The most difficult and dangerous part of the work was yet to come – the sinking of the shaft. By 31 May this had reached a depth of 25ft. more than a quarter of the intended 80ft., from the bottom of which a bore would go down a further 200ft.

The same issue of the *Advertiser* announcing these facts, gave information about the Stoneferry engine, started by Ald. Mayfield on 2 April. The tremor had been so great that the valve had to be replaced and the engine restarted on 2 May, but it did not reach its intended ten strokes per minute. Delays in the supply of pipes slowed down the making of the Springhead-Stoneferry connection, but the actual works at Springhead were going on very smoothly and more quickly than expected.

On 14 July, 1862, the spring water was sent for the first time through the pipes to Stoneferry.

It was an occasion of great rejoicing, marked by merry peals of church bells starting at an early hour and continuing at intervals throughout the day. The ceremony was to be about two o'clock in the afternoon. The Mayor and most of the Corporation assembled at the Town Hall, then went by carriage, cab or omnibus to the springs. At the lane leading from Anlaby Road to Springhead, the Mayor's carriage was hailed by 250 workmen (in their best clothes) who wanted to remove the horses and pull the carriage themselves. They were checked in their zeal as the Mayoress was in the carriage and the Mayor would not allow the human cavalcade to take over. The workmen therefore marched ahead accompanied by a band. The unfinished buildings were bedecked with flags, but, as the *Advertiser* put it, 'The place where the important event of the day was to be performed was not remarkable for its conspicuousness by anything but an old white table on which to place the enormous key.'

The Mayor gave the works but a brief glance before handing the key to Ald. Mayfield to do the honour. 'They owed to Mr. Matthewson and to Mr. Warden a deep debt of gratitude for obtaining this supply' (Cheers). Sadness was expressed that Mr. Matthewson was too ill to

The ironstone pillar in Pearson Park was given by Messrs. Bolckow and Vaughan of Middlesbrough, who supplied the pipes connecting Springhead and Stoneferry.

attend, for he would have been delighted. William Warden had been invited by the Waterworks Committee and the Mayor said he was glad of it, for it showed that they appreciated 'that which he had endeavoured to do.' The water now flowing by gravity towards Stoneferry was only the overflow from the Springs and the Mayor 'trusted that there would be enough for all purposes' when the new scheme was in full working order.

Mayfield spoke in passing of the differences of opinion there had been and hoped that every unpleasant feeling would be buried in oblivion.

Warden was 'pleased and proud.' There was not yet enough water, but he was sure there would be abundance for years to come. Dale said that about 2 million gallons were running at that time. He paid tribute to the workmen; there had never been a serious fall-out and, he was happy to say, very little cursing and swearing and drinking.

The civic party went to the tent where the workmen were to dine – a treat given by the Committee at Dale's suggestion – to see all was as it should be, then drove on to Stoneferry to watch the water come into the reservoir. Here they were met by a band, and, after viewing the works, had luncheon served in a tent near the new engine house. Several ladies were present.

Among the many toasts was one by Mr. Wells to Mr. Matthewson, whose constitution, it was said, 'was broken down under care, anxiety and trouble.' A man of innate modesty, his merits were not brought before the town before it was too late, commented the *Advertiser*.

THE SPRINGHEAD WATERWORKS

The range of buildings we see today at Springhead, is considerably larger than the waterworks planned and created by Thomas Dale in the early 1860s. His buildings comprised an engine house, an ornamental tower, boiler house, coal bins, smith's shop, store-rooms, cottage, stables and other out-buildings.

The site Dale had to use was within the confines of the land owned by the Corporation; it was necessarily at the edge of the chalk where the springs rose to the surface and because of twenty years sporadic experiment there, with springs still producing water, he did not have a clear flat field upon which to build. Nowadays one can visit the site in its new role as the Yorkshire Water's Museum with barely a feeling there is water under the ground.

The new works were constructed independently of the old bores as a new shaft 80ft. deep with a borehole from the bottom of it, was to be sunk in the centre of the engine-house. Dale put it as far to the north-east as possible for geological reasons and it lay between the Old Springs and the former bores. This meant that the boiler house was built over the Old Springs, which therefore had to be arched over and covered. Dale's engine house is the building at right angles to the present Museum's engine house, where

Springhead Waterworks. The part to the right of this picture was Dale's engine house.

Photograph: Mr. A. McTurk. By kind permission of the Senior Keeper, Mr. D. W. Atkinson

Springhead Waterworks: Warden's Well.
Photograph: Mr. A. McTurk. By kind permission of the
Senior Keeper, Mr. D. W. Atkinson.

the magnificent Woodhouse engine, a Cornish beam engine of 1876, is the dominant exhibit.

Dale's engine house, where now three electric pumps stand like Daleks, is not part of the Museum, nor open to the public. In its early days, it housed two smaller Cornish engines, named after Aldermen Jackson and Fountain. The chimney was somewhat to the east of the present buildings, a landmark on this rising ground, until demolished in 1907.

Dale gave details of the meticulous care taken to ensure the foundations were firm and secure. Excavations for the engine-house foundations began on 25 March, 1862, and the first stone footing placed on 4 April. It was night and day work '. . . and so rapidly did the work go on that in three weeks from the commencement of getting out the excavation . . . upwards of 100,000 bricks had been built in cement, in the construction of centre walls, side walls and engine beds, the whole resting on strong Elland stone footings, varying from 20 to 30 superficial feet each on the bed and 12 inches thick, the whole of the materials used being of the best description,' as Dale wrote in his Report to the Waterworks Committee on completion of the works on 26 February, 1864.

Dale certainly pushed things forward. Mr. Smalley, the contractor for laying the foundations of the engine house, a large area, 15ft. deep, had said he could not get it done in under three weeks, but Dale insisted it be done in ten days as he wanted the bricklayers to start. By working night and day, the large gang of workmen finished the foundations a mere nine days later. At one time during this work, Mr. Smalley felt the brickwork under his feet rise up and water bubbling between the bricks. He called to Dale, who got a large number of men to put a big stone slab on the bricks to prevent the water bursting out. It was covered with cement, bricks and tallow, stopping up every crevice through which water might burst – a three hour job. This prompt action prevented the probable destruction of all the work to date and showed what an immense quantity of water there was in the neighbourhood of the springs.

An old temporary shaft which had to be avoided in making new foundations, was only three feet from them. It held water to a depth of 25ft. and was discharging at the rate of one million gallons a day. The strata upon which Dale was working here were compact and with careful timbering at crucial points and the construction of a coffer dam to hold back the water from the Old Springs, this phase of building was completed 'without even the aid of a hand-pump.' The foundations were strengthened with iron bars, each 6ft. x 4ins. x ³/₈ ins, turned up at one end and down at the other to bond with the brickwork. Today, the nearness of 'Warden's Well' to the outer wall of the building is a positive reminder of Dale's problems.

The engine house was 80ft. x 16ft. (smaller than the later one) and 42ft. high. The tower was 10ft. square inside and 60ft. high to its stone cornice.

Difficult as was the construction of foundations, dealing with the Old Springs, and, more especially, the sinking of the shaft within the engine house were more so.

Pumping started at the borings on 28 April, 1862, and they were bared in 30 hours at 25 feet, discharging in the process 2 million gallons of water. Debris at the bottom was cleaned out, uncovering a base of soft rubbly chalk into which an iron rod could be pushed to a depth of 9 feet. So rafts made of balks of hard Baltic timber, fastened together with iron straps and bolts and then cradled on to 6ft. elm planking were put down on the chalk at the bottom of the springs to provide foundations for retaining walls of cement. Again this was round the clock work, using two 12 h.p. steam engines and pumps.

Parts of the springs were arched over, but the areas which would have to bear the greatest weight of the boilers, etc., were walled in with brickwork up to 3ft. of the boiler house floor and then a large stone landing, 12 inches thick, placed on top. There was a brick basin into which the Springs discharged.

Much of this work had not been contemplated by Dale. It added to the time and the cost, but as he put it, he had had 'to combat with engineering difficulties of no ordinary character, the whole length of the bottom of the Old Springs being one immense discharge of water with a soft, slutchy, rubbly chalk foundation . . .' The ground between the Old Springs and the engine house was soft and boggy, so it was covered with 3ft. of concrete to take the rest of the boilers. This, too, was not in the original estimate.

The sinking of the shaft was contracted out to Thomas Clark of London, but the first time Clark went to see the situation at Springhead, he jibbed at the problems to be faced and said it would cost more than his tender of £1,000 because of the risk. Negotiations with and straight talking from the Town Clerk, informing Clark that if he did not sign and fulfil the contract in the exact terms of the tender, the Committee would get the work done themselves, made him toe the line. After all, as Pearson had said at the Stoneferry pipe-laying ceremony, it was a time when work was slack.

A start was made on Monday, 12 May, 1862. The shaft was circular, of

14ft. diameter and eventually 71ft. 6ins. deep. The expected difficulties were come upon – a lot of loose chalk and great quantities of water, as well as the bearing down upon the shaft's edge of the immense weight of the brick and stone foundations of the engine house floor.

Sheet piling shored up the sides of the shaft, but strong jets of water shooting through cracks in the piling had to be caulked with hemp and tallow. Once through the band of marl they came to the same soft chalk as at the bottom of the springs and then, from 30ft. downwards, strong rubble chalk from which the water flow was greater. From this point, a lining of cast iron cylinders was lowered by their own weight on vertical rods held by cross-bearings supported at the top of the shaft. Sheet piling coated with gas tar continued to be employed and the space between it and the iron cylinders filled with concrete made of small clean gravel and Lias-lime, making sure it went into all the crevices. It hardened like masonry, Dale reported. The data of previous shafts at Springhead had led Dale to believe that at 40ft. down they would come to solid chalk not needing to be lined, but as the chalk they encountered in this shaft was very loose, a brick lining set in cement 9ins. thick, was put in until the desired depth was reached. As with the sheet piling, water forced its way sideways into the shaft and left large cavities under the building. Working as quickly as possible, these holes were filled with brickwork and concrete. Openings were also made in order to insert girders to support the pumps: very arduous work as it was well beneath the foundations.

Working conditions were so bad, the men were paid double wages and worked only four hours at a time. They were given half a pint of rum per man per shift, as they were working under a constant cascade of water. Two men were employed all the time drying clothes in a nearby hut.

Once at the required depth of about 80 ft, the bottom of the shaft was covered with 1½ins. thick cast metal plates, fastened together with water-tight joints and resting on cross-girders. Both girders and plates passed under the brickwork lining. A guide pipe, 10ft. long, was fixed into the centre of the plates; it had a funnel-shaped top into which a 5-ton conical iron plug could be inserted. The flow of water could thus be stopped for repairs etc., as the other bores and springs would provide sufficient outlet for water normally coming up at this point.

On 5 July, 1863, the borehole was begun, with yet more round-the-clock working. As expected, many flints of varying thickness were passed through, the flow of water increasing each time.

About a month later a foot-thick flint was penetrated at 235ft. from the surface and as the rate of flow immediately increased to 3 million gallons per day, the Jackson engine was put to full speed. The borehole was then 210ft. below the bottom of the shaft, that is, about 290ft. from the surface.

On 29 January, 1864, both Jackson and Fountain engines were set to work together, the Springhead Waterworks was in operation and Thomas Dale concluded his report by stating with great pleasure, 'that the whole of these works have been executed without loss of life or any serious accident occurring.'

The river water was shut off on Thursday evening, 28 January, 1864, and henceforth, it was said in the Waterworks Committee meeting of 3 February, the town would be exclusively supplied by the Springhead water. This was not precisely what happened for within days river water was let into the reservoirs as a prudent measure against night fires, but with the assurance from Ald. Mayfield that 'not a drop of river water had been sent into the town.'

So concluded an important chapter in the history of the water supply of Kingston-upon-Hull, but it is a saga without end.

As in legends of old three aspirants came in turn. The first, Wicksteed, dismissed the springs' capacity with little testing. The second, Simpson, tested more effectively, but his mind was elsewhere. Then came the local man, William Warden, who, after great difficulties, and with the help of Matthewson, prevailed, showing that the springs could provide a large quantity of water for the town. Warden is remembered today, his reputation reinstated because of the swift and efficient building of Springhead Waterworks by Thomas Dale, who to my mind is the real hero of the episode.

But there are other minor characters whose names we shall never know, who constantly gave the Waterworks Committee and the Town Council something to think about regarding the water being supplied to the general public. To 'Civis' and 'Timothy Nervous', to the 'Man who has had his tea spoild tonight' and to many others we owe our thanks, as a water supply is a matter of concern and vigilance for everyone who receives it.

ACKNOWLEDGEMENTS

Because much of the material for this book was gleaned from old Hull newspapers in the Albion Street Local History Library, I must thank the staff there for their unfailing help and courtesy. My thanks are also due to the City Archivist, Mr. G. Oxley, and his assistant in the Record Office.

Photographs in the book bearing no acknowledgement are my own, some of them prepared from my old colour transparencies in the capable hands of Richmond and Rigg, Photographers, of South Church Side. I owe a deep debt of gratitude to Mr. Alick McTurk who willingly took photographs at Springhead and in the Guildhall. Permission for these was given by Mr. D. W. Atkinson, the Senior Keeper at Yorkshire Water's Museum at Springhead, and by Mr. Kevin Robinson for the Chief Executive Officer's department at the Guildhall. I was taken round the Guildhall by Miss Pat Griffiths in my search for portraits of former Town Councillors and Mr. McTurk was given material assistance by Mr. David Bell of the Guildhall staff.

Permission for the reproduction of these photographs and also of the diagrams in the former Kingston upon Hull Corporation's booklet on the Water Department, came from Mr. Robinson and Mr. Atkinson.

I wish to thank all these people as they have eased the way through a very lengthy but enjoyable project.

Monument to John Jaques Matthewson in the South Transept of Holy Trinity Church. It depicts Moses striking water from the rock.

Photograph: Richmond and Rigg.

SOURCES

I went through local newspapers dated from the mid 1830s to the mid 1860s; some were quoted more than others. The papers were: *The Rockingham, The Packet,* the *Eastern Morning News* (in the 1890s), and more especially, *The Eastern Counties Herald,* the *Hull Advertiser* and the *Hull Free Press*.

For general and background material I consulted:

Broxap, Ernest: *The Sieges of Hull during the great Civil War.* From English Historical Review, Vol. 29, July 1905.
Kingston upon Hull Water Undertaking, 5th Centenary 1447-1947. Booklet published by Kingston upon Hull Waterworks.
Mortimer, J. R., *The chalk water supply of Yorkshire,* Excerpt Minutes of Proceedings of the Institute of Civil Engineers, Vol. lv, Session 1878-9 part i, printed 1879.
Sheahan, J. J., *History of the Town and Port of Kingston upon Hull.* 1866.
Sheppard, June A., *Draining of the Hull Valley.* East Yorkshire Local History Society booklet No. 8.
Smith, Rev. William, *Ancient Springs and Streams of the East Riding of Yorkshire.* A. Brown and Sons Ltd., 1923.
Szabadvary, F. *History of Analytical Chemistry,* Pergamon, 1966.
Transactions of the Hull Scientific and Field Naturalists' Club: Sheppard, T., *Some glimpses of old Hull in the light of recent excavations.* Vol. IV Part IV. 1912. Slade, Rev. H. P., *Our Water Supply,* Vol. I No. II. 1 December 1899.
White's *Directories* for 1826, 1838, 1839, 1840.

For more detailed reports and personal recollections:

Eccles, C. S., *History of the Springhead Waterworks,* printed by Pybus and Sons, Hull 1901.
Dale, Thomas, *Report on completing the New Works at Springhead.* 26 February 1864.
Matthewson, J., Lecture: *The Water we drink,* printed by James Plaxton, Hull, 1861.
Mayfield, J. W., *History of Springhead and how the Pearson Park was obtained for the People.* A. Brown and Sons Ltd. 1909.
Mr. Pearsall's Report, *Examination of the Water of the River Hull,* 23 August 1842.
Suddaby, John, *Hull and its Water Supply,* 1905.
Water Committee Report, 15 August 1842 (contains Wicksteed's preliminary report).
Wicksteed, Thomas: *Report on the proposed work for supplying the Borough of Kingston upon Hull with water,* 14 April 1843, to which is appended Mr. Aikin's *Report to the Water Committee,* 13 February 1843.

Also many miscellaneous letters in the Hull Record Office shed light on the details of the story of how the Springhead Waterworks eventually came into being.

Thomas Dale's gravestone in the Spring Bank General Cemetery; the stone has been removed since this picture was taken in 1973.